Action
Maths

www.two-canpublishing.com

Published by Two-Can Publishing,
43-45 Dorset Street, London W1U 7NA

© 2002, 2000 Two-Can Publishing

For information on Two-Can books and multimedia,
call (0)20 7224 2440, fax (0)20 7224 7005, or visit our website at
http://www.two-canpublishing.com

'Two-Can' is a trademark of Two-Can Publishing.
Two-Can Publishing is a division of of Zenith Entertainment Ltd,
43-45 Dorset Street, London W1U 7NA

HB ISBN 1-85434-695-4
PB ISBN 1-84301-091-7

HB   2 3 4 5 6 7 8 9 10 04 03 02
PB 1 2 3 4 5 6 7 8 9 10 04 03 02

SHAPES, MEASURE, PATTERNS & GAMES
Consultants: Wendy and David Clemson
Editor: Diane James
Photography: Toby
Text: Claire Watts

SHAPES & MEASURE
Editorial Assistant: Jacqueline McCann
Design: Beth Aves
Words marked in **bold** are explained in the glossary.

Printed in Hong Kong by Wing King Tong

CONTENTS

Shapes

6 Shapes Around You

Everything you look at has a shape! Some things are curvy. Some are straight. Some have points or corners. What words do you use to talk about the shapes around you?

Look at all the shapes on these pages. Can you describe them? How many curved edges do they have? How many straight edges do they have?

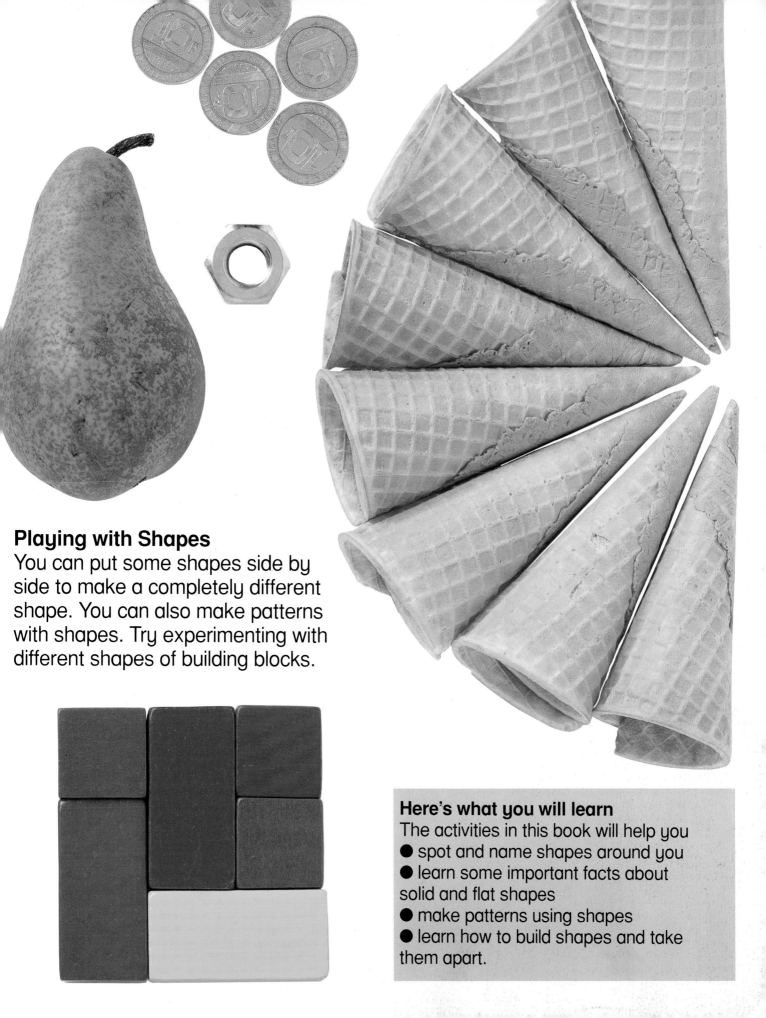

Playing with Shapes

You can put some shapes side by side to make a completely different shape. You can also make patterns with shapes. Try experimenting with different shapes of building blocks.

Here's what you will learn
The activities in this book will help you
● spot and name shapes around you
● learn some important facts about solid and flat shapes
● make patterns using shapes
● learn how to build shapes and take them apart.

8 Printing Shapes

Look for objects with interesting shapes which can be used to print a pattern or a picture. To print the picture here, we used a sponge, a cork, a rubber and a wooden building block. How many other shapes can you find to print with?

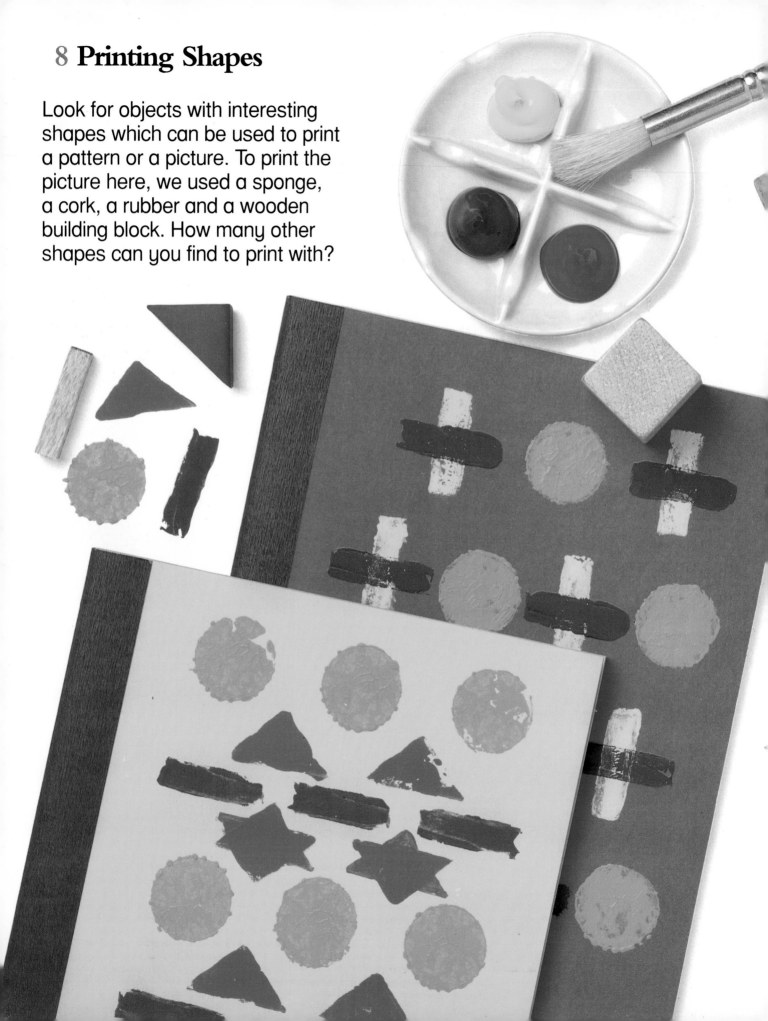

● Cover one side of your shape with paint. You could use a paintbrush, or dip the shape in the paint. Press it carefully on to the paper.

Some shapes fit together with no gaps in between, like these squares. Which of your shapes fit together? Which shapes do not fit together?

Here's what you learn
Printing shape pictures helps you
● recognize different shapes
● discover how shapes fit together.

10 Making Shapes

Here are some simple ways to make basic shapes from coloured paper.

Square

● Start with a rectangle of paper.
● Place the paper so that one of the short ends is towards you.

● Fold the top left corner towards you until the top of the paper lines up with the right-hand side of the paper.
● Cut off the single piece of paper left at the bottom.
● Open out the paper and you will have a perfect square.

Triangle

● Cut your square straight down the diagonal fold to make two triangles.

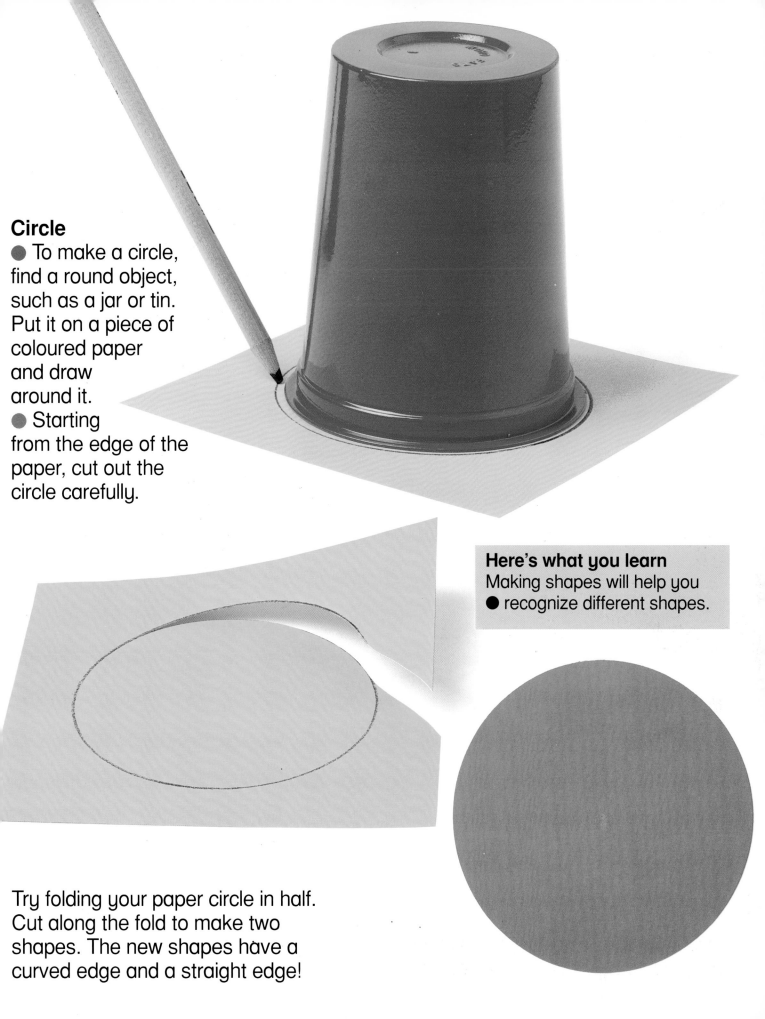

Circle

● To make a circle, find a round object, such as a jar or tin. Put it on a piece of coloured paper and draw around it.

● Starting from the edge of the paper, cut out the circle carefully.

Here's what you learn
Making shapes will help you
● recognize different shapes.

Try folding your paper circle in half. Cut along the fold to make two shapes. The new shapes have a curved edge and a straight edge!

12 Shape Pictures

We made the picture here using coloured paper shapes. You will be surprised at how easy it is to make an interesting picture of your own. Cut, or tear, a collection of different paper shapes before you start.

Try It Out

● Arrange your shapes on a sheet of paper to make a picture that you like.

● Don't stick the shapes down straight away. You may decide you want to move them around! When you are happy with your picture, carefully lift each shape up and glue it in place.

Circles and ovals are good shapes for making heads and bodies. Triangles, rectangles and squares are good for making buildings.

Here's what you learn
Making shape pictures helps you
● fit shapes together
● use different shapes in design.

14 Patches

With just a few old scraps of fabric you can make a colourful piece of patchwork. The six-sided shape below is called a hexagon. Trace around it to make a pattern and use this to help you make lots of paper hexagons.

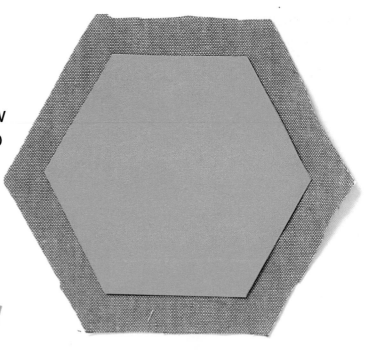

● Place each paper hexagon on a piece of material. Cut around the paper leaving extra material on all sides.

● Fold each edge of the material over the paper and pin it down. When you have pinned a few pieces you are ready to sew the hexagons together!

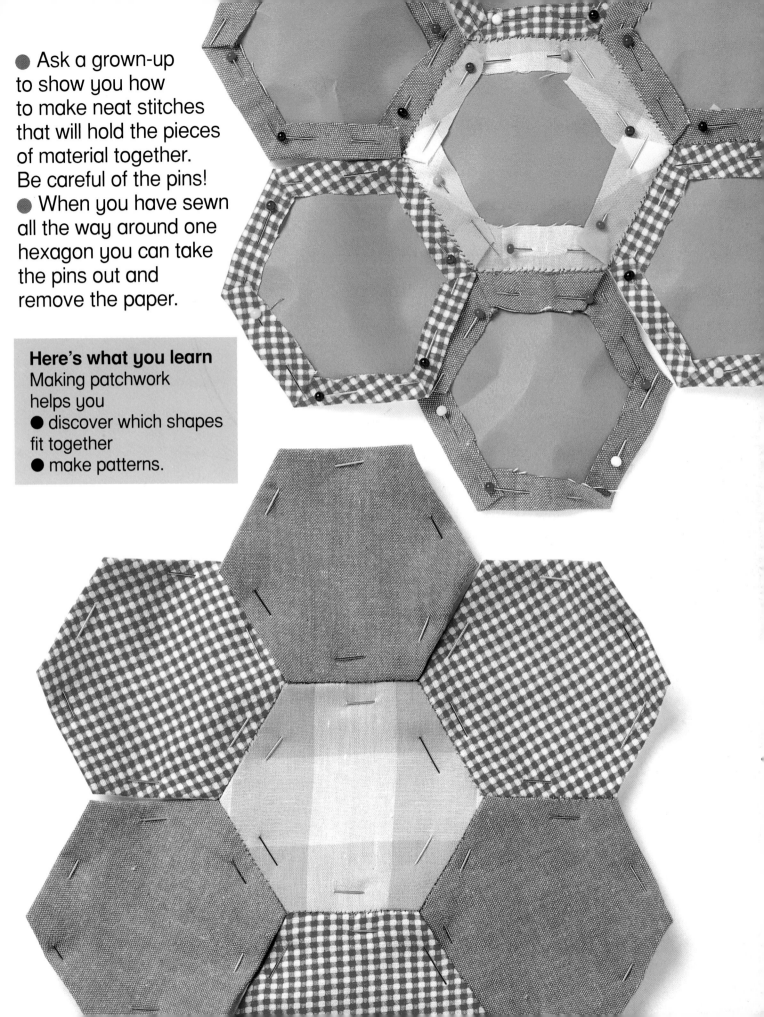

● Ask a grown-up
to show you how
to make neat stitches
that will hold the pieces
of material together.
Be careful of the pins!
● When you have sewn
all the way around one
hexagon you can take
the pins out and
remove the paper.

Here's what you learn
Making patchwork
helps you
● discover which shapes
fit together
● make patterns.

16 Cut-Out Shapes

You can make these amazing shapes just by folding paper and making cuts in the folded edge.

Fold and Cut

● Fold a piece of paper in half down the middle.

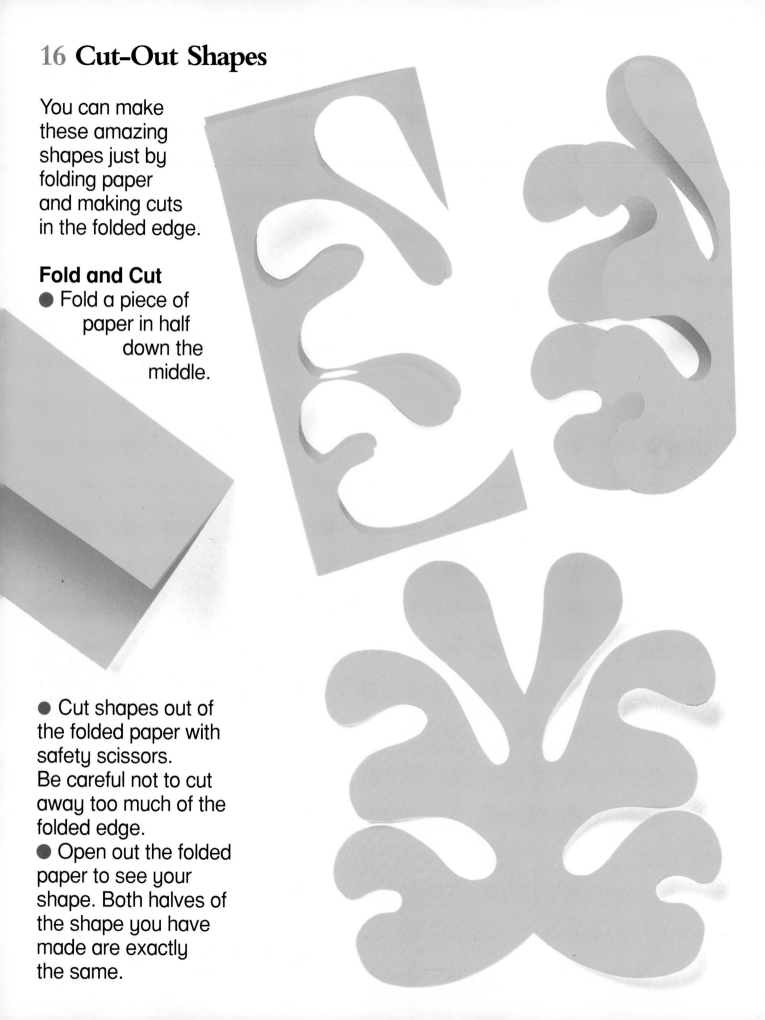

● Cut shapes out of the folded paper with safety scissors. Be careful not to cut away too much of the folded edge.

● Open out the folded paper to see your shape. Both halves of the shape you have made are exactly the same.

Four Folds

● Now try folding the paper in half, and then in half again.

● Cut shapes from both folded edges, but remember not to cut off too much!

● When you unfold the paper you will find that the right and left sides match, and the top and bottom match, too.

Here's what you learn
Making cut-out shapes helps you
● think about symmetry.

18 Slit and Slot Shapes

Here is a way to make flat shapes stand up.

● Cut some different shapes from stiff card. You could use the shapes here to trace around, or draw your own.

● Make two short cuts in one side of a card shape, as close together as possible.

● Carefully remove the strip of card in between. You will be left with a short slit.

● You can make more than one slit in each shape, but it is better if they are on different sides.

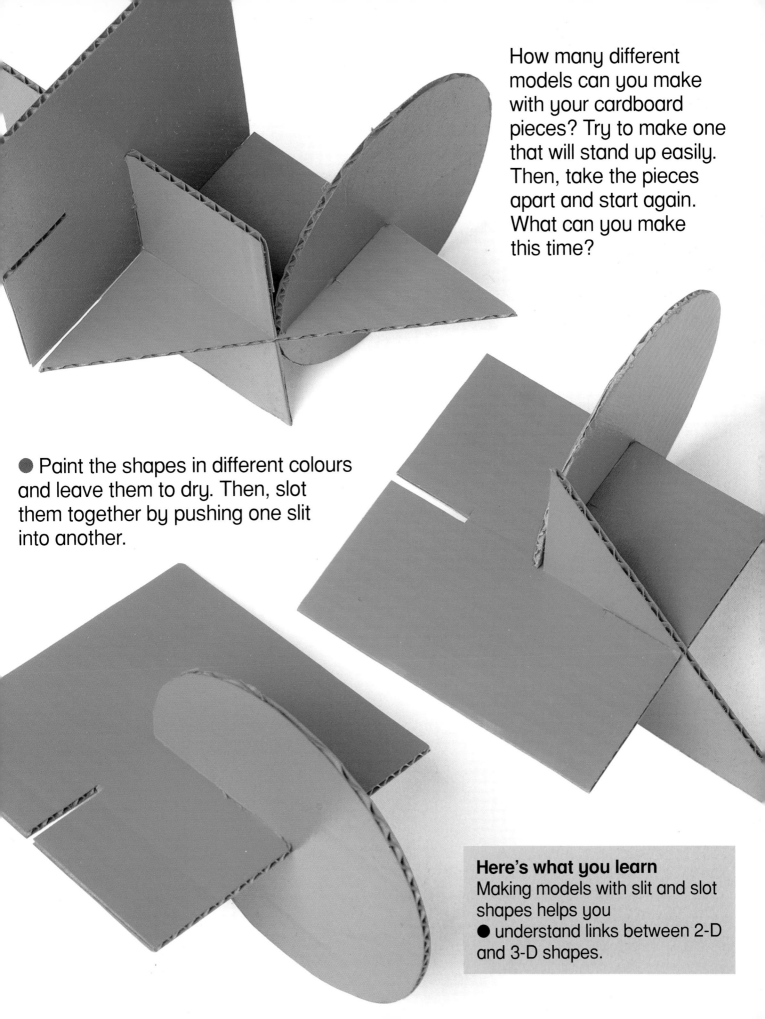

How many different models can you make with your cardboard pieces? Try to make one that will stand up easily. Then, take the pieces apart and start again. What can you make this time?

● Paint the shapes in different colours and leave them to dry. Then, slot them together by pushing one slit into another.

Here's what you learn
Making models with slit and slot shapes helps you
● understand links between 2-D and 3-D shapes.

Once you know how to slit and slot, you can make all sorts of models that stand up by themselves. Use thick paper or thin card to make your models.

Slit and Slot Bushes

Draw two bush shapes about the same size and cut them out. Cut a slit from the bottom of one shape to the middle. Then, cut a slit from the top of the other shape to the middle. Paint the shapes in bright colours. Slot them both together and stand the bush up.

Tall Trees

Draw two tree shapes. You could use the tree here as a guide to trace around. Cut the shapes out. Make slits in both trees, as you did for the bushes. Now stand the tree up.

Palm Trees

For these trees, cut out some
large, leafy branch shapes. Cut a slit
half-way through each branch near
one end. Make slits in the top of a
cardboard tube and slot in the branch.

Stand-Up Crocodile

Cut out the shape of a crocodile's body.
Then, cut out two leg shapes. Paint all
the pieces. Make two slits in the base
of the body and one in the top of each
leg. Stand your crocodile
up by slotting the pieces
together!

Now arrange your trees and bushes to make a jungle scene. You can make tall or short trees by using different sized cardboard tubes.

Hanging Bird

Make a bird to keep the crocodile company. You will need three pieces – one for the body, one for the wings and one for the head.

Try making other sorts of plants. Can you think of any other slit and slot animals to put in your jungle?

You can make all sorts
of scenes using slit
and slot shapes in the
same way.

24 Food Monster

Look at all the different shapes of vegetables on this page. Some of them are very strange! Can you think of a way to describe them? Try making a funny food monster to decorate your table. Look out for round shapes to make the eyes and nose, and long shapes for arms and legs.

● Ask a grown-up to help you join the vegetables together using cocktail sticks. Watch out for sharp points!
● Push one end of a cocktail stick into a vegetable.
● Then, push another vegetable on to the other end of the stick.

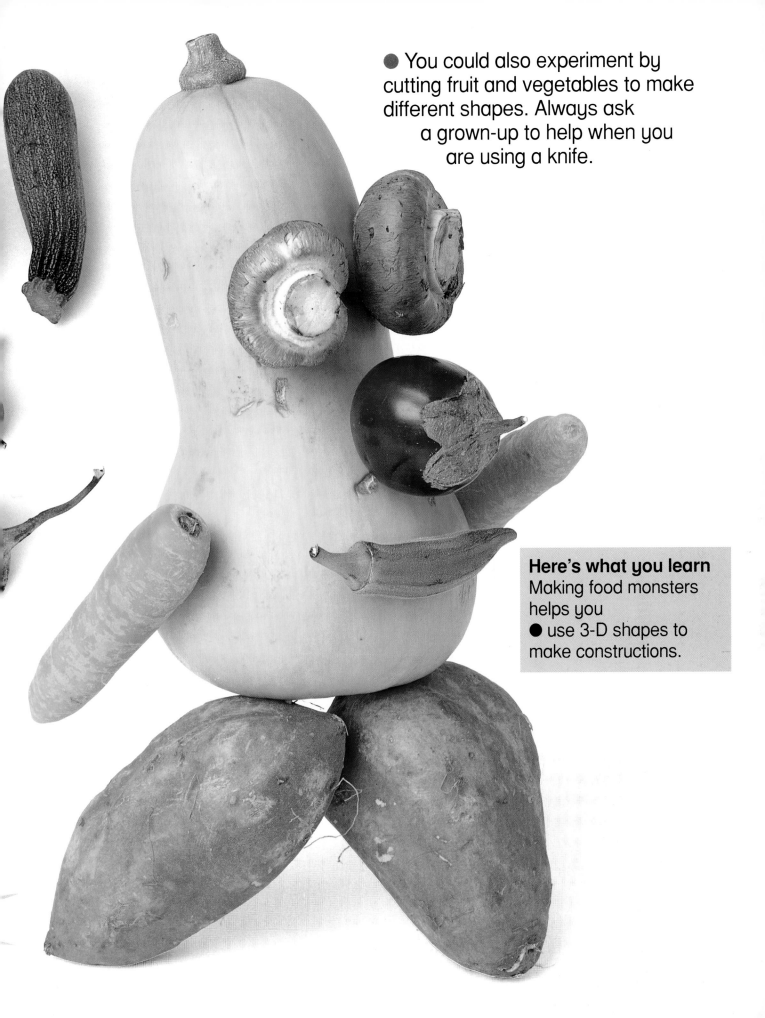

● You could also experiment by cutting fruit and vegetables to make different shapes. Always ask a grown-up to help when you are using a knife.

Here's what you learn
Making food monsters helps you
● use 3-D shapes to make constructions.

Containers come in lots of shapes and sizes. The next time you are in a shop, have a look to see how many different shapes you can spot.

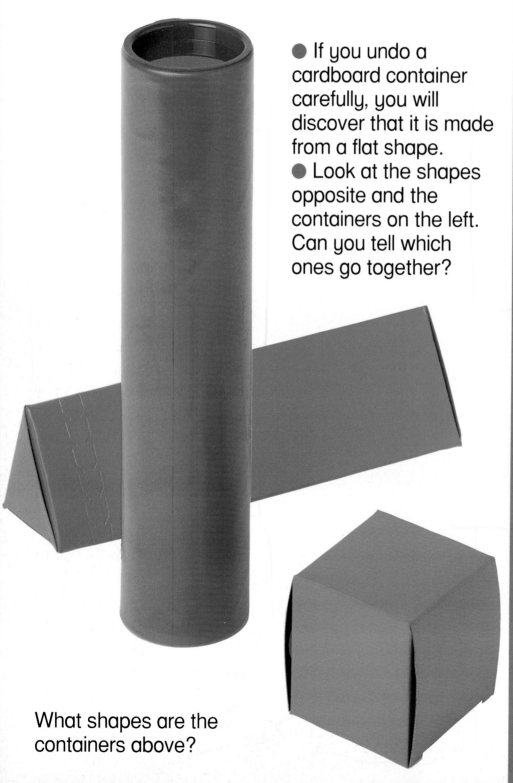

● If you undo a cardboard container carefully, you will discover that it is made from a flat shape.

● Look at the shapes opposite and the containers on the left. Can you tell which ones go together?

What shapes are the containers above?

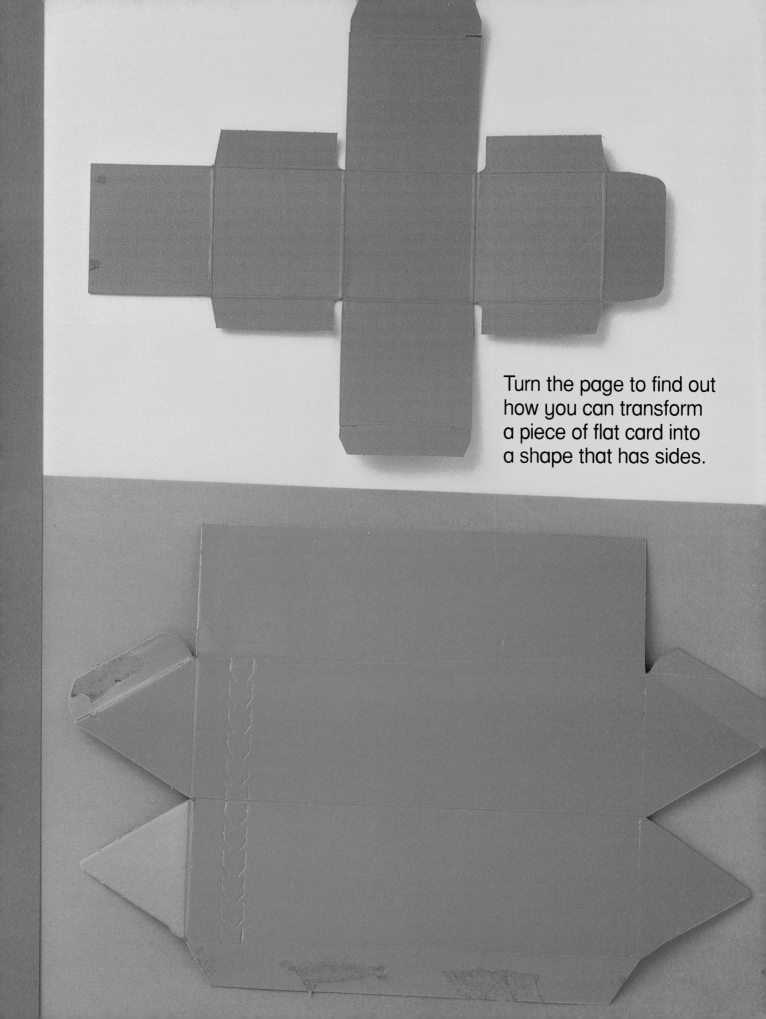

Turn the page to find out
how you can transform
a piece of flat card into
a shape that has sides.

On the last two pages we looked at what some containers look like when they are opened out. If you follow the instructions here, you will be able to turn a flat piece of card into a cube.

● Trace the shape on this page. Use your trace to cut out the same shape from a piece of thin card.

● Use a pencil and ruler to draw in the dotted lines, using the picture as a guide.

● You need to make the shape as accurate as possible so that all the sides of your cube will fit together.

The three narrow strips with shaped corners are called tabs.

● Fold the card along each of the dotted lines keeping the pencil marks on the inside of the cube.

Fold the longest strip over to meet the tab on the opposite side. Glue the tab and press it firmly on to the strip from the inside. Then, glue the tab on one of the other sides. Tuck the tab in and press it from the inside. Fold the last flap up to make the lid of the box. Tuck it in without gluing.

Here's what you learn
Making a cube helps you
● find out about the flat shapes, or nets, that make up a box
● draw and cut accurately.

30 Pencil Holder

You should be able to find cardboard tubes in lots of different shapes and sizes. They are often used for packaging, or inside rolls of paper and tin foil. Make a collection of tubes and turn them into a useful storage unit for your pencils, scissors and rubbers.

● Arrange your painted tubes in a group and glue them together at the sides.

Sorting

● First, decide which tubes are best for the things you want to store in them. For example, your pencils may need a long, thin tube. If necessary, you could ask a grown-up to cut a tube to make it shorter.

● Paint the tubes in bright colours.

● Make a base for your pencil holder by gluing the ends of the tubes to a piece of card. Fill the holder with all your pencils, pens and crayons.

Here's what you learn
Making and painting a pencil holder helps you
● think about the idea that similar shapes come in different sizes.

Build an Animal

Our colourful animal was made from used cardboard boxes and tubes. Start collecting as many different things as you can. Look for interesting shapes, with both curved and straight edges. If you are using containers which have had food in them, make sure you clean them first!

You can use sections cut from boxes to make different shapes.
Can you see how we made the triangle for the animal's nose? What do you think the round shape is made from?

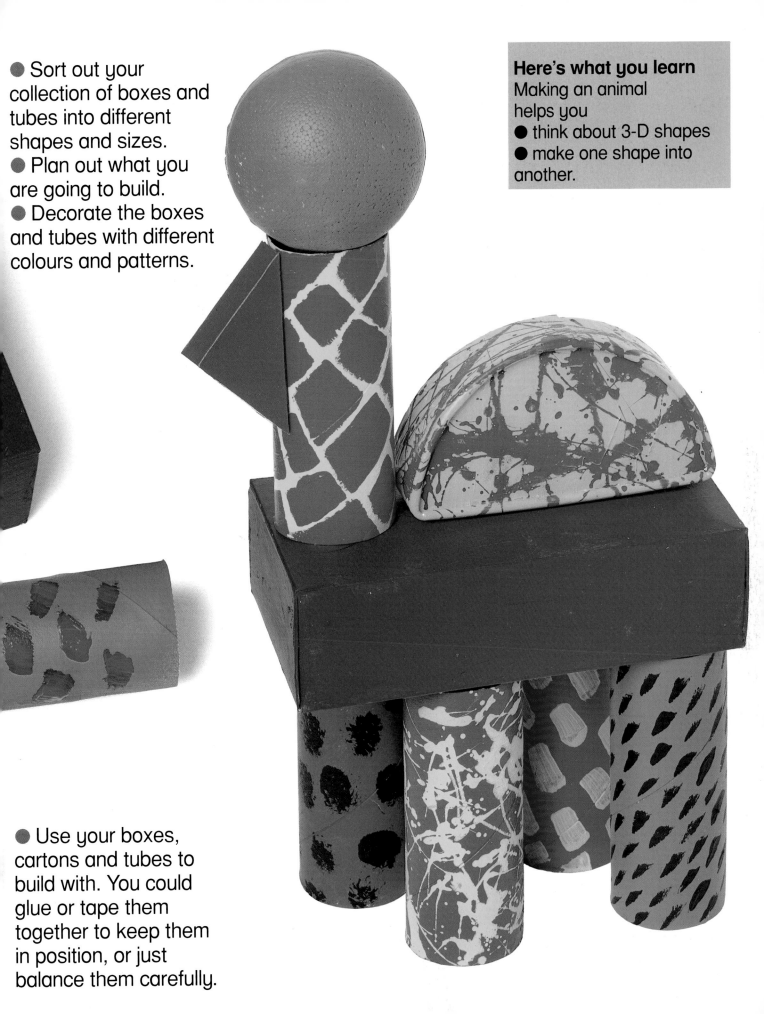

● Sort out your collection of boxes and tubes into different shapes and sizes.
● Plan out what you are going to build.
● Decorate the boxes and tubes with different colours and patterns.

● Use your boxes, cartons and tubes to build with. You could glue or tape them together to keep them in position, or just balance them carefully.

Here is a way to turn flat pieces of paper into completely different shapes that you can wear. Your friends will be amazed! You will need long strips of paper in two different colours.

Concertina Folds

● Glue the ends of two strips of paper together at right angles. Look at the picture at the top.
● Then, fold the underneath strip over the top strip.
● Next, fold the strip which is now underneath over the top one.
● Carry on folding until all the paper is finished.
● Glue the end down.

Gently pull the two ends of the paper to open out the chain a little. When you let go, the shape will spring back. To make a longer piece, glue extra strips of paper on to the end of the chain.

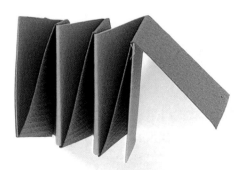

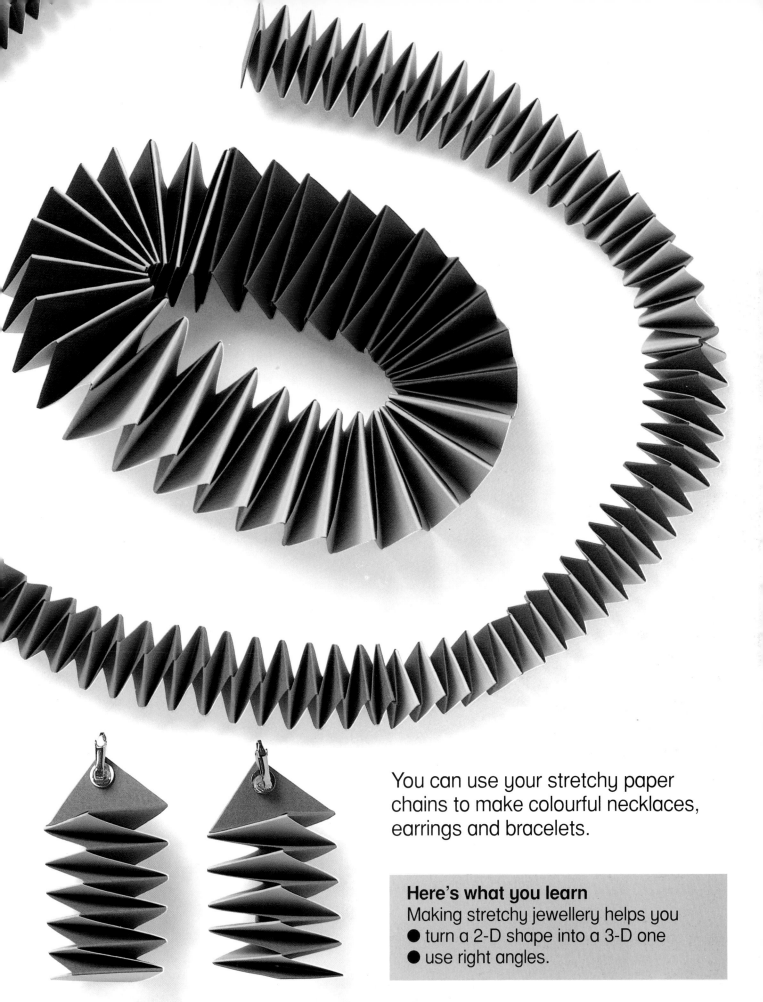

You can use your stretchy paper chains to make colourful necklaces, earrings and bracelets.

Here's what you learn
Making stretchy jewellery helps you
● turn a 2-D shape into a 3-D one
● use right angles.

Measure

38 What Size Is It?

Everyday, we ask questions, such as 'How big is it?' 'How tall is it?' 'How heavy is it?' Or, 'What time is it?' All of these questions have something to do with measuring. In this book we will be looking at lots of different ways of measuring.

We use words such as big and small, tall and short, or heavy and light to describe things around us.

Look at the groups of objects on these pages. Which is the biggest in each group? Which is the smallest? Which is in the middle?

Here's what you will learn
Measuring is one of the most important maths skills we need to learn.
The activities in the book will help you
● explore height, length, weight, area and volume
● use measures.

40 How Tall Are You?

Make your own height chart so that you can measure yourself.
● Stick several lengths of coloured paper together to make one long strip that is taller than you.
● Use a building block as a guide to measure lines at equal distances apart down the side of the paper.

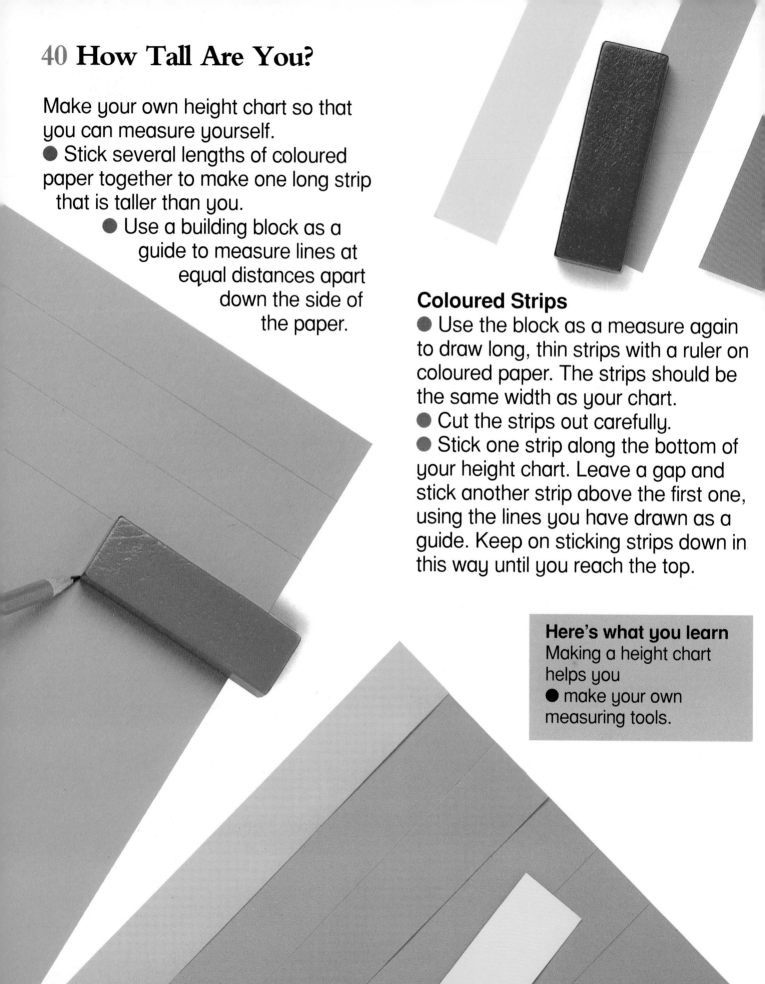

Coloured Strips

● Use the block as a measure again to draw long, thin strips with a ruler on coloured paper. The strips should be the same width as your chart.
● Cut the strips out carefully.
● Stick one strip along the bottom of your height chart. Leave a gap and stick another strip above the first one, using the lines you have drawn as a guide. Keep on sticking strips down in this way until you reach the top.

Here's what you learn
Making a height chart helps you
● make your own measuring tools.

● Fix the chart to
the wall so that the
bottom touches
the floor. Stand
next to it and
ask someone
to make a
mark above
the top of your
head. Count the
number of strips
from the floor up
to the mark. Now
measure your friends
against your chart.
Who is the tallest?
Who is the
shortest?

How big is your hand? Here is a way to make a hand puppet that will fit you perfectly!

Make a Pattern

● Put one of your hands flat on a piece of felt. Draw a mitten shape slightly larger than your hand on the felt.

● Cut out the mitten shape. Then, place it on a different coloured felt and trace around it. Cut the second shape out. Now you have two different colours for the front and back.

● Place one felt shape on top of the other. Ask a grown-up to help you sew around the edge. Use brightly coloured thread to sew the pieces together.

● Now you are ready
to decorate your puppet.
Can you guess what
these puppets are going
to be? Turn the page
to find out.

Here's what you learn
Making these animal
puppets helps you
● investigate the idea
of area
● compare sizes
● match shapes.

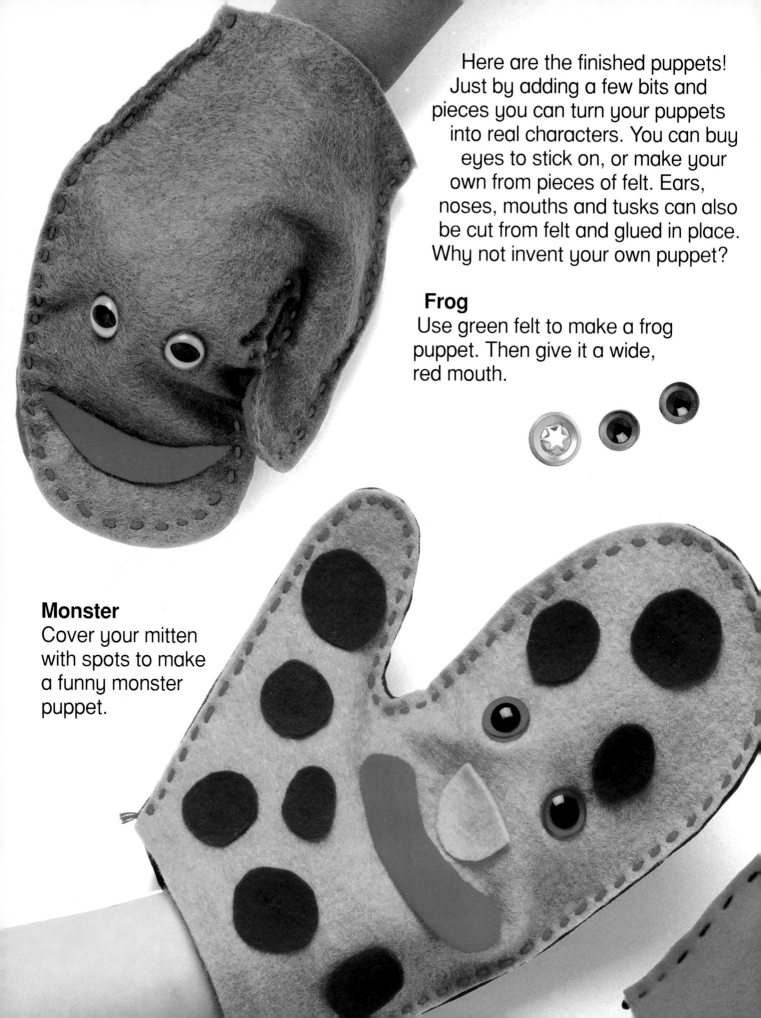

Here are the finished puppets! Just by adding a few bits and pieces you can turn your puppets into real characters. You can buy eyes to stick on, or make your own from pieces of felt. Ears, noses, mouths and tusks can also be cut from felt and glued in place. Why not invent your own puppet?

Frog
Use green felt to make a frog puppet. Then give it a wide, red mouth.

Monster
Cover your mitten with spots to make a funny monster puppet.

Elephant
Use grey felt to make ears and a trunk for an elephant. Then add a pair of tusks to finish it off.

Shape Face
Make a face using squares for eyes, a triangle for the nose and a long, thin rectangle for the mouth.
This puppet looks a bit like a robot!

Finger Puppets

Here is an easy way to make a different sort of puppet that will fit on your finger.

Bird Puppet
● Cut a small paper circle. Make a cut from the edge into the centre.
● Fold the paper round to make a cone and tape the edge.
● Tape the cone on to the paper tube.
● Cover the paper tube and cone with several layers of paste and pieces of torn newspaper.
You can make the paste by gradually mixing water into flour until it is thick and creamy.

Making a Tube
● Take a long strip of paper, or thin card and wrap it quite tightly around your finger.
● Tape the end and then pull the tube off your finger gently.

● When your puppet is dry you can paint it. Why not make a puppet to fit every finger!

Mexican

● Once again, make a tube that fits your finger.

● To make the hat, cut a paper circle. Ask a grown-up to help you make some small slits in the centre of the circle. Push the circle over the paper tube to make the brim of the hat.

● Cover the tube and brim with paper and paste as before. Now it is ready to paint.

Here's what you learn
Making finger puppets helps you
● follow instructions
● compare lengths and areas.

48 Cut-Out Mask

We used a paper plate to make our mask. You will need to know where to make holes for your eyes, nose and mouth. Here is a good way to take the measurements.

Measure It Out

● To measure the distance between your eyes, hold a length of wool in front of your face, stretching from the middle of one eye to the middle of the other. Then, lay the wool in the middle of your mask and mark each end.

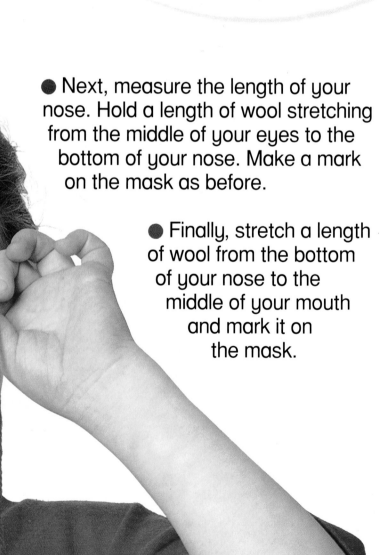

● Next, measure the length of your nose. Hold a length of wool stretching from the middle of your eyes to the bottom of your nose. Make a mark on the mask as before.

● Finally, stretch a length of wool from the bottom of your nose to the middle of your mouth and mark it on the mask.

● Make a small hole on each side of your mask, roughly half way up. Thread a length of string through each hole and make a knot in the end so that it cannot pull through. Now you can decorate your mask!

Making the Mask
● Ask a grown-up to help you cut holes where you have marked the eyes and mouth.
● You can cut a hole for your nose, or make a flap by leaving one edge attached to the mask.

Once you know how to make a basic mask, you can decorate it in all sorts of different ways.

Tiger
● First, paint a stripy tiger face on your mask.

● Next, cut out some paper ears, paint them, and stick them to the top of the mask.

Bird

To make the feathers for your bird mask, cut out shapes from coloured paper.

Stick the shape with the large feathers on first and then add the small feathers. You can make the beak by folding a piece of card and gluing it in place.

Here's what you learn
Making masks helps you
● use measurements.

Here is a way to make a card doll and a whole wardrobe full of paper clothes. First, draw the outline of a person on card, or trace around the doll below. Ask a grown-up to help you cut it out. Now you can make some clothes for your doll.

Making a Shirt

● Place the doll on coloured paper and draw a shirt shape around the top half of the body.

● Lift the doll off and draw some tabs on the top of the shirt at the shoulders.

● Ask a grown-up to help you cut out the shirt and tabs. Put it on the doll and bend the tabs over the doll's shoulders, to hold it in place.

Making a Cap
● Draw a cap shape a bit bigger than the doll's head.
● Ask a grown-up to cut a slit in the cap like the one shown below. Push the doll's head through the slit.

Here's what you learn
Making these dolls helps you
● match sizes and shapes
● investigate the idea of area.

Making Trousers
● Place the doll on a different colour of paper and draw around the bottom half of it.
● Lift the doll off and draw a pair of trousers slightly larger than the doll's legs. Add some tabs at either side of the waist.

54 Bottle Band

It is hard to believe, but you really can make your own band with some empty glass bottles, water, a metal spoon and a beaker to use for measuring.

● Make a mark a little way up an empty plastic beaker.
● Fill the beaker with water up to the mark. We added a little food colouring to the water to brighten up our bottle band!
● Pour the water from the beaker into the first bottle. You may need a jug or a funnel to help.

● Pour two measures from the beaker into the second bottle.

● Now pour three measures into the third bottle, four into the fourth bottle and finally five into the fifth bottle.

● Play your bottle band by knocking gently on the sides of the bottles with a metal spoon.

Here's what you learn
Making a bottle band helps you
● measure customary units.

The bottle with most liquid in it, makes a low sound. But, the bottle with the least liquid, makes a high sound.

56 Mobile

This colourful mobile looks great hanging up, but the trick is to make it balance!

Cardboard Cut-Outs

● Cut out some shapes from cardboard. You could trace around the ones on this page, or make up your own.

● Decorate both sides of the shapes.

● Ask a grown-up to make a hole in the top of each shape and thread a piece of string through it. To make this easier, use a sewing needle with a large eye.

● You can also decorate balls to hang on your mobile. We used craft balls which you can buy in shops. They are very light and it is easy to thread string through them, using a sewing needle.

Hang It Up
● Attach a length of string to the middle of a long stick or piece of dowel.

Tie the objects to the stick in different places. Once you have done this, you will have to slide them along the stick until the mobile balances. You may also have to adjust the lengths of the strings.

Here's what you learn
Making mobiles helps you
● find out about weight and balance.

When you are baking, it is very important to measure out exactly the right amount of each ingredient. Otherwise things may not turn out as you expect. Ask a grown-up to show you how to use some measuring scales.

You Will Need:

175 grams plain flour
50 grams sugar
100 grams butter
2 drops vanilla essence

● Ask a grown-up to heat the oven to 170°C (325°F, gas mark 3).

Mix It Up!

● Put the flour and sugar into a mixing bowl.

● Cut the butter into small pieces and add it to the bowl. Use your fingertips to rub the butter into the flour.

● When the mixture looks like fine bread crumbs, add the vanilla essence. Use your hands to make the mixture into a large dough ball.

Roll It Out!

● Knead the dough on a surface sprinkled with flour.

● When you have a smooth, firm ball, use a rolling pin to roll it into a thin, flat shape, about as thick as a coin.

● Cut shapes using a biscuit cutter.

● Put the biscuits on a greased baking tray and bake them for 20 minutes.

● Ask a grown-up to take the biscuits out of the oven and put them on a wire tray to cool.

Here's what you learn
Baking biscuits helps you
● follow instructions
● use standard measures.

60 Biscuit Boxes

When you have made your biscuits, you might want to give some away as a present. Here are two ways of making boxes to pack them in.

Pile Them Up

● Put one of the biscuits on a piece of card. Using a ruler, draw a square slightly bigger than the biscuit. Cut out two squares exactly the same size. These will be the top and bottom of the box.

● Decide how many biscuits you want to give away and pile them up. Stand a piece of card against the pile to measure the height. Make a mark on the card.

● With the help of a ruler, draw a card rectangle, slightly taller than the pile of biscuits, and the same width as the square you have already cut out. Cut four rectangles exactly the same size. These will be the sides of the box.

● Tape together the bottom and sides. Put the biscuits in the box and tape the last square on to make the lid.

Spread Them Out

● Lay six biscuits flat on a piece of card and draw a rectangle around them. Cut out two rectangles the same size.

● Cut four thin strips of card the same length as each edge of the rectangle.

● Tape the strips to the rectangle to make the sides of the box.

● Tape the other rectangle on one side to make the lid.

Here's what you learn
Making biscuit boxes helps you
● investigate the ideas of area and volume.

62 Wrapping Boxes

Make some wrapping paper for your box by decorating some plain paper with paint.

Paint and Paper
● First, choose a piece of paper that you think will be big enough to cover the box.
● Splatter some paint on to the paper using a brush, or dab it with a sponge dipped in paint.

Wrap It Up!
● When the paint is dry, lay the paper decorated side down and place the box in the middle of it. Fold the long sides of the paper around the box.

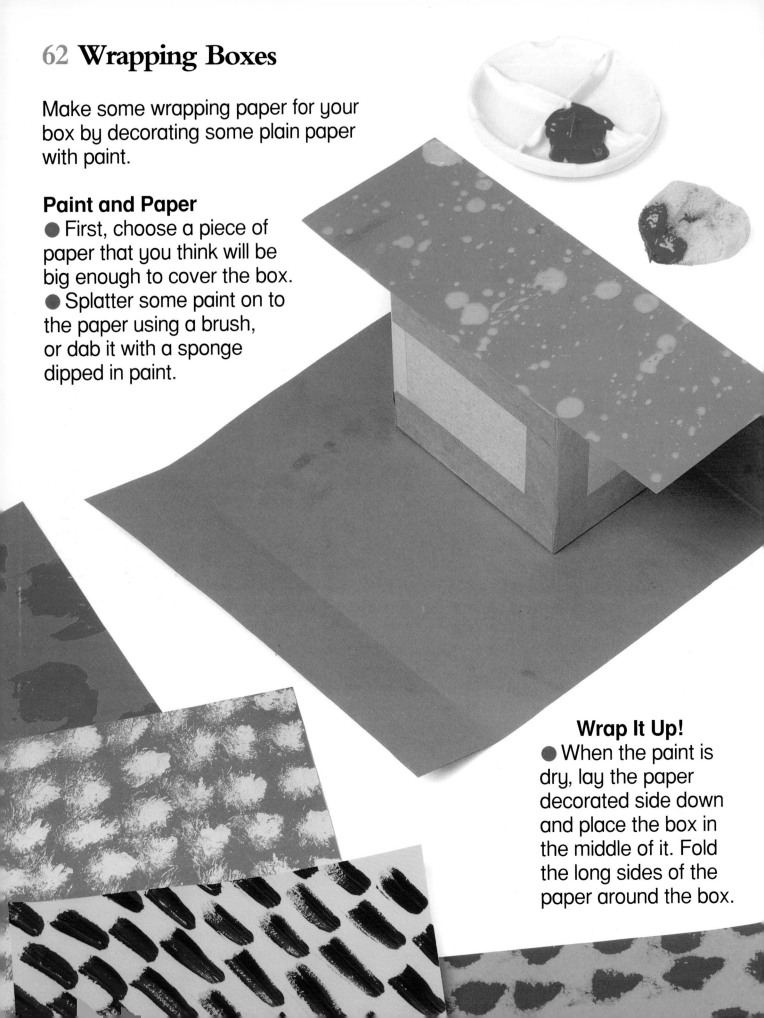

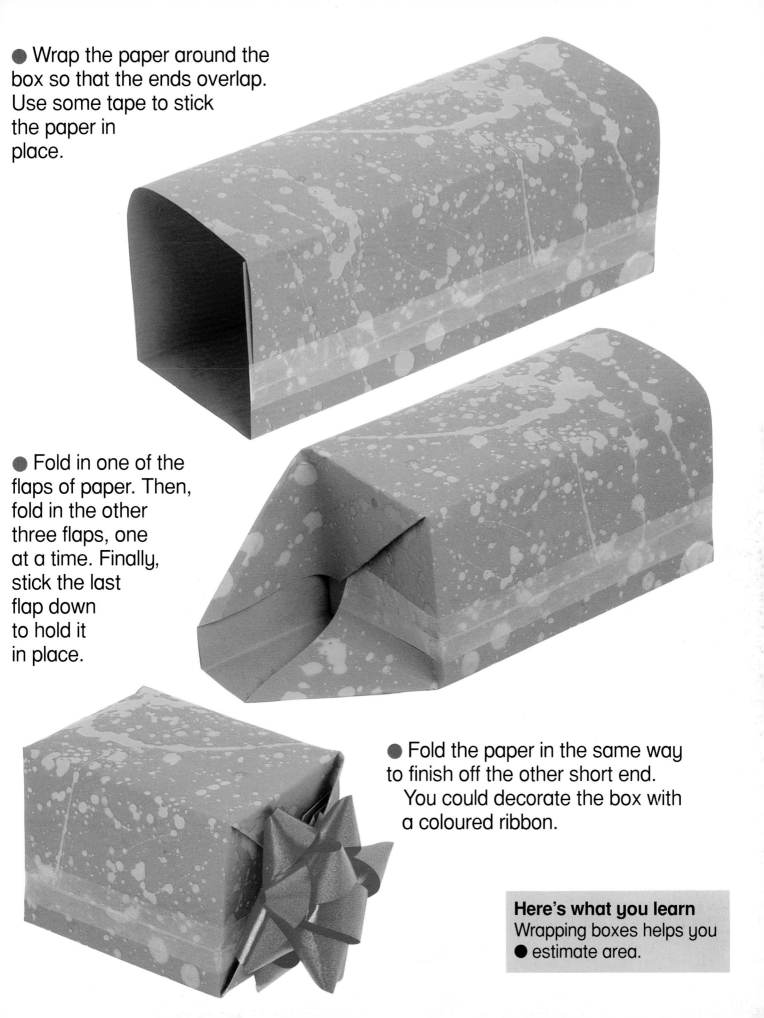

● Wrap the paper around the box so that the ends overlap. Use some tape to stick the paper in place.

● Fold in one of the flaps of paper. Then, fold in the other three flaps, one at a time. Finally, stick the last flap down to hold it in place.

● Fold the paper in the same way to finish off the other short end. You could decorate the box with a coloured ribbon.

Here's what you learn
Wrapping boxes helps you
● estimate area.

64 Sand Timer

Here's a way to measure how much time something takes.

Paper Cone
● Draw a big circle on a piece of stiff paper. You could use a dinner plate to draw around.

● Cut out the circle. Then, ask a grown-up to help you cut a slit from the edge of the circle to the centre.

Here's what you learn
Making a sand-timer helps you
● understand how we measure time.

● Fold one side of the slit around the other to form a cone shape, like this. Tape it in place.
● Cut a tiny hole in the bottom of the cone.

A Line of Triangles

Cut out some matching paper triangles and glue them in a line up the side of an empty bottle.

Falling Sand

● Place the cone in the top of the bottle and fill it with sand. Watch the sand fall through the cone and fill up the bottle. The sand gradually reaches each triangle mark.
● Get a friend to hop around the room once, while you watch the timer. How many marks does the sand pass? Now it's your turn – are you slower, or quicker?

A tangram is the name for a square which is cut into pieces. The pieces can be put together to make different patterns or pictures. Look at the pictures here. Can you find a small square and five triangles in each picture? The black shape is called a parallelogram. Can you spot it in all of the pictures?

Making a Tangram
● Ask a grown-up to cut out a square from thick card.
● Use a ruler and pencil to mark out the shapes you can see in the picture.

● Cut along the lines and paint each piece a different colour.

How many pieces make up the tangram? Mix them all up. How many pieces can you count now?

Use your tangram pieces to make a dog shape like this one. Can you see the dog's ear? Can you find its tail? Have all the tangram pieces been used to make the dog shape?

Now try to make a person running, like this one, or a bird like the one below. Re-arrange all the pieces to make a picture of your own. You must use all of the tangram pieces somewhere in your picture.

Back Together Again!
When you have finished, mix all the pieces up again.
Can you use them to put the square back together again?

Here's what you learn
Playing with tangrams helps you
● investigate the idea of area
● create pictures using shapes.

Patterns

70 Looking at Patterns

There are patterns all around us. You can find them in paving stones, in the stitches of your jumper and on a butterfly's wings. A pattern is made when shapes or numbers are put in a sequence and repeated.

Look around you. How many different patterns can you spot?

Here's what you will learn
We use patterns to help us make sense of the world. Maths is all about patterns. The activities in this book will help you
● sort things into groups
● match similar things
● find out how things fit together.

Make a patterned snake to hang from your ceiling.

Painting a Spiral

● Draw a spiral on a piece of card. Start from the edge of the card and gradually spiral in towards the centre. You may need to draw a few spirals for practice first.

● Cut the snake out starting from the end of the spiral on the edge of the card.

● Paint a snake pattern on your spiral, or decorate it with coloured paper.

● Ask a grown-up to thread a piece of cotton through the middle of the spiral. Now hang your snake up.

Here's what you learn
Making and decorating spirals helps you
● create repeating patterns
● change a flat shape into a three dimensional one.

74 Beads

Threading beads is a good way to make a pattern. Look around your home or school for things to use as beads. Here are some ideas for making your own beads.

Paper Beads

● Glue together two pieces of coloured paper. Tear out a triangle shape. Roll the shape around a pencil and stick down the narrow end.

● Make a simple paper bead with a long strip of coloured paper. Roll it around a pencil, then stick down the end. You could decorate the paper before making your beads.

Pasta Beads

● Pick pasta shapes with holes in the middle.
● Paint the shapes with poster paints and leave to dry.

Clay Beads
● Use the type of clay which dries by itself to make these beads.
● Make a small ball of clay and ask a grown-up to make a hole in it with a knitting needle or cocktail stick.

Sort Them Out
How many different types of beads have you collected?
● Sort the beads into different colours and shapes.

Here's what you learn
Making and sorting beads helps you
● sort things into different groups or categories
● match similar things.

Beads to Find!
If you look, you should be able to find lots of things to use as beads. We used straws, plastic beads and even peanuts. Can you think of anything else you could use?

Threading Beads

Now you can try making some
patterns with your beads.

● Use string or shoe-laces to thread
the beads into a necklace.

● Pick two sorts of beads. Thread one
sort, then another on to the string.

● Look at the patterns on this page?
Can you make up your own bead
patterns?

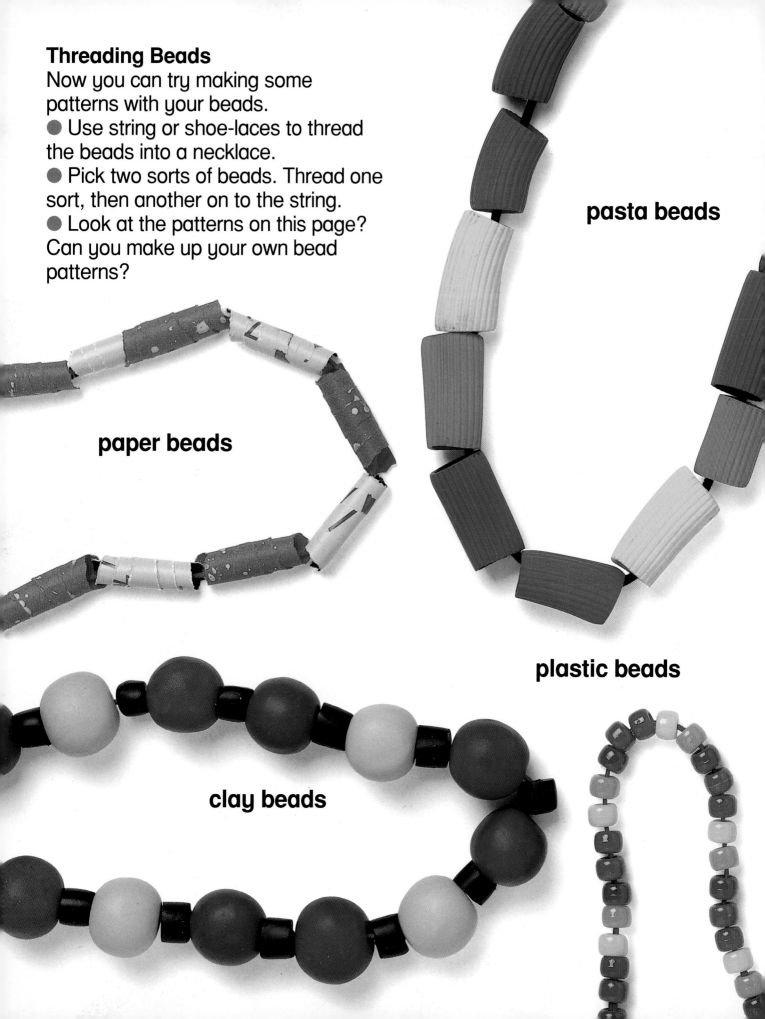

pasta beads

paper beads

plastic beads

clay beads

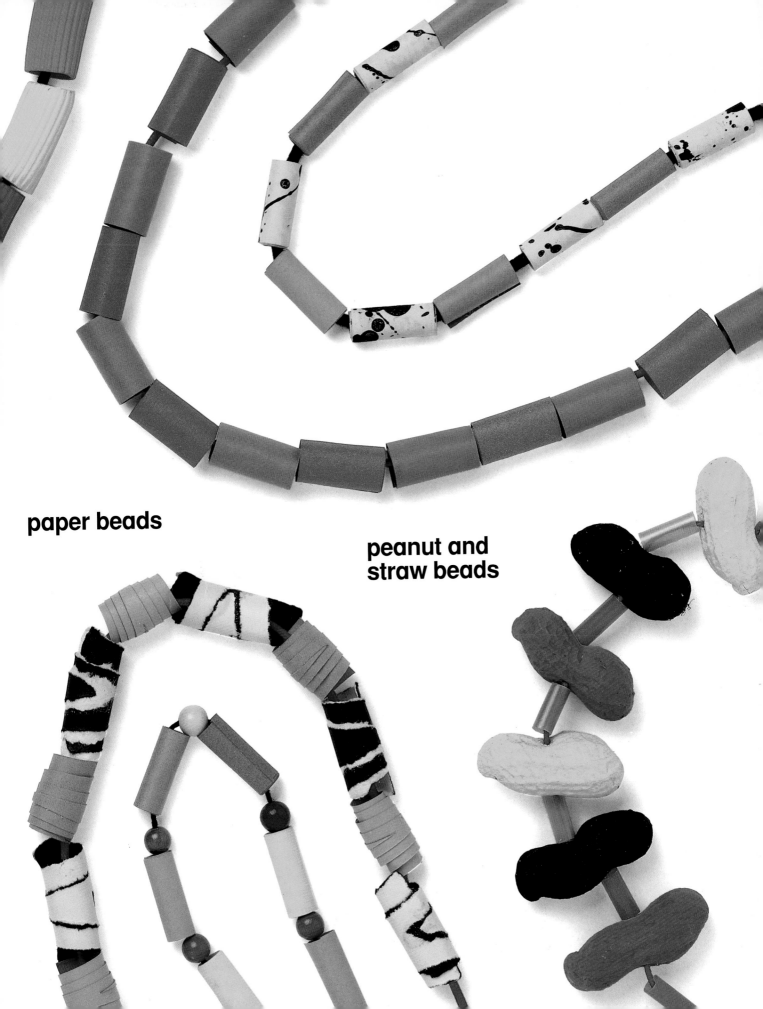

paper beads

**peanut and
straw beads**

Here's a delicious way to play with patterns! Ask a grown-up to help you cover the top of a cake with soft icing. Use a collection of sweets to decorate the top.

Shapes and Colours

First decide which sweets you are going to use. Which ones look good together? Which are your favourites?

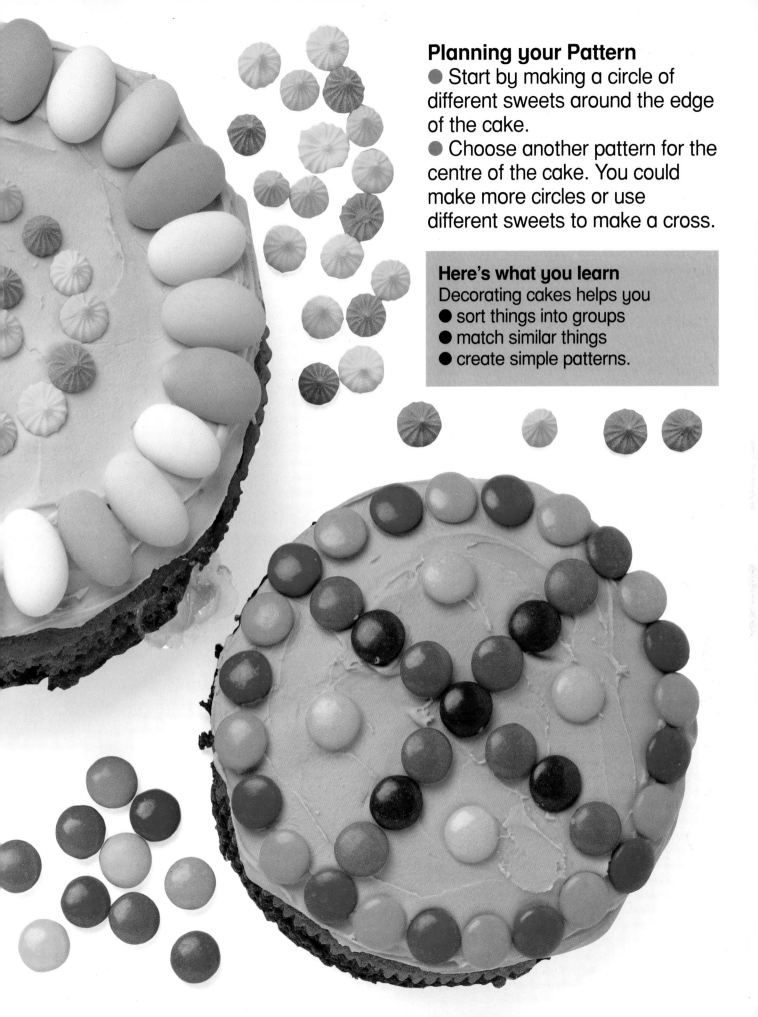

Planning your Pattern

● Start by making a circle of different sweets around the edge of the cake.

● Choose another pattern for the centre of the cake. You could make more circles or use different sweets to make a cross.

Here's what you learn
Decorating cakes helps you
● sort things into groups
● match similar things
● create simple patterns.

Some of the clothes you wear are made from woven fabrics. These fabrics are made on large machines called looms. You can do your own weaving at home using a cardboard loom. Use brightly coloured wool or strips of felt. Can you see the pattern the threads make?

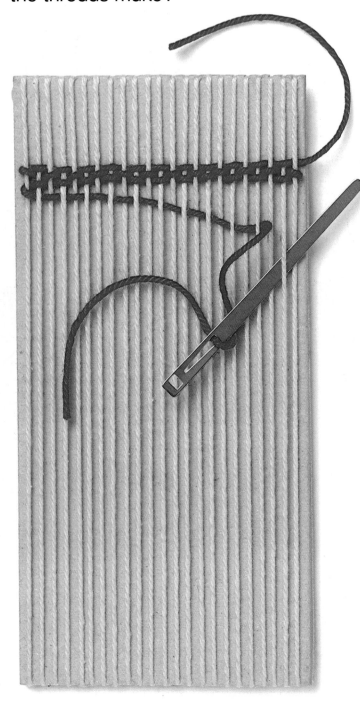

Loom
● Ask a grown-up to cut a small piece of card and make notches in both ends
● Wind a length of wool around the card. The notches will keep it in place. Tie the ends of the wool at the back.

Over and Under
● Ask a grown-up to thread a large, blunt needle with a length of wool.
● Push the needle under and over the threads until you reach the other side.
● Weave back the other way, under the threads you went over before, and over those you went under.

Here's what you learn
Weaving helps you
● create simple patterns
● use ideas about symmetry.

You can make a pattern with woven paper too! Find some fairly stiff coloured paper to weave with.

Simple Pattern
● Fold a piece of paper in half.
● Make a row of cuts along the folded edge. Unfold the paper.
● Cut some strips of another colour. Weave these strips over and under the slits you have made.

Diagonal Stripes
● Take another piece of paper and make diagonal cuts. Weave strips through the slits. Does the pattern look the same?

Here's what you learn
Paper weaving helps you
● create patterns and shapes.

Wavy Stripes

Ask a grown-up to cut wavy slits in a piece of paper. You will also need some wavy strips of another colour. Weave the strips as before.

Tartan Stripes

Cut two slits close together in a piece of folded paper. Leave a gap, then cut two more slits close together and so on. Weave thick and thin strips of coloured paper in and out of the slits.

Zig-zag Stripes

Ask a grown-up to make zig-zag slits in the paper with a craft knife. Weave straight strips through the slits.

84 Dot Patterns

Here's another way to make patterns with wool.

Glue Patterns

● Make a pattern with a few dots of glue on a piece of card.
● Take a length of wool. Press one end into the glue.
● Guide the wool around the glue pattern, pressing it down as you go.

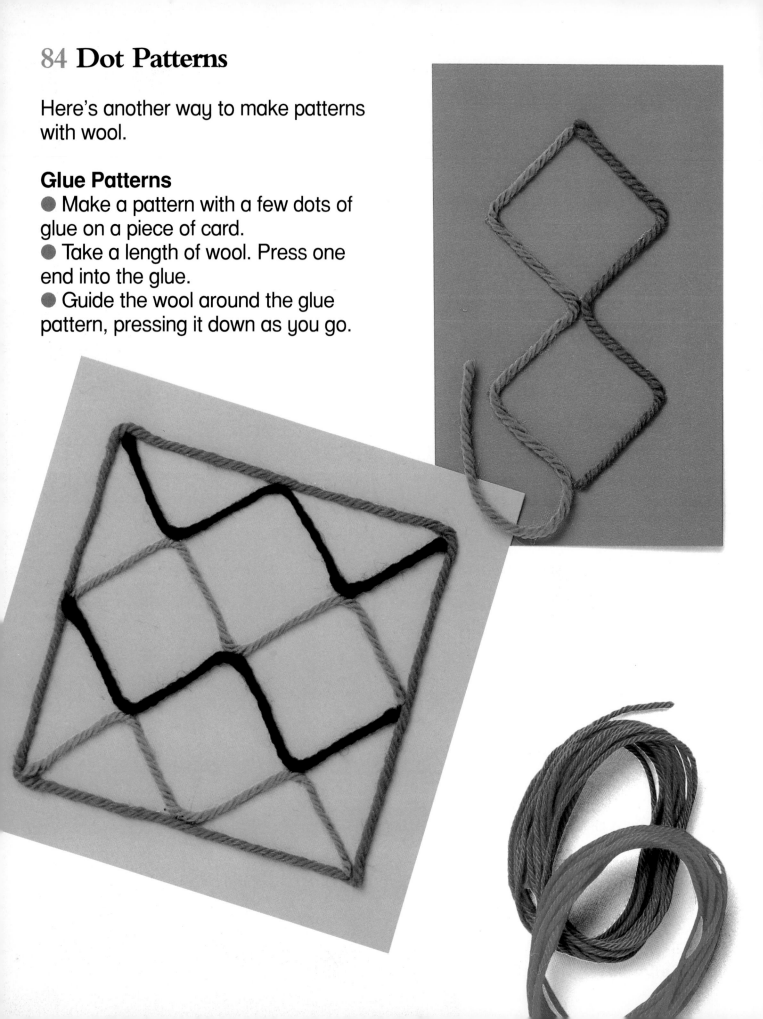

Pin Patterns

● Ask a grown-up to arrange a pattern of pins on a piece of strong card.

● Take a length of wool and tie it carefully to one of the outside pins.

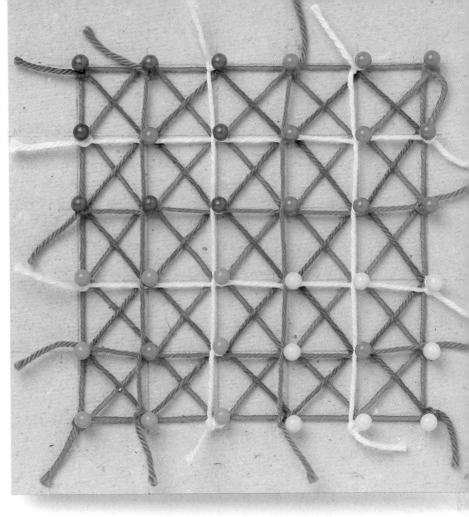

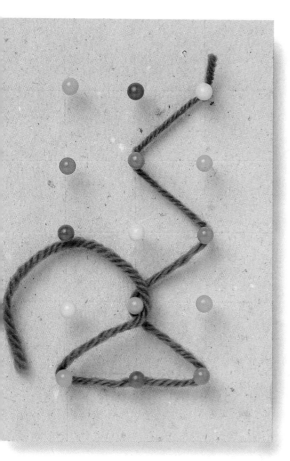

● Stretch the wool around the pins, twisting it to keep it in place. When you reach the edge, tie the end of the wool, and cut off any extra.

Here's what you learn
Making dot patterns helps you
● think up patterns
● create shapes.

86 Paper Cuts

You can make some amazing patterns by folding and cutting paper.

Fold and Cut
● Fold a piece of paper in half and then in half again. Cut a small piece out of one edge. Unfold the paper.

● To make a more complicated pattern, make several cuts along the edges before unfolding the paper.

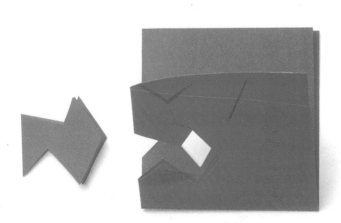

Concertina Folds

● Cut a long strip of paper.
Make folds backwards and forwards,
so the strip opens out like a concertina.
● Make cuts in the folded paper.
● Open the paper out.

Here's what you learn
Making paper cuts helps you
● create patterns
● discover symmetrical patterns.

88 Tiles

Each of these tiles has a very simple design, but you can arrange them to make all sorts of patterns.

Designing the Tiles
● Ask a grown-up to cut out some squares of card, all the same size.
● Choose a simple design and paint each square exactly the same.

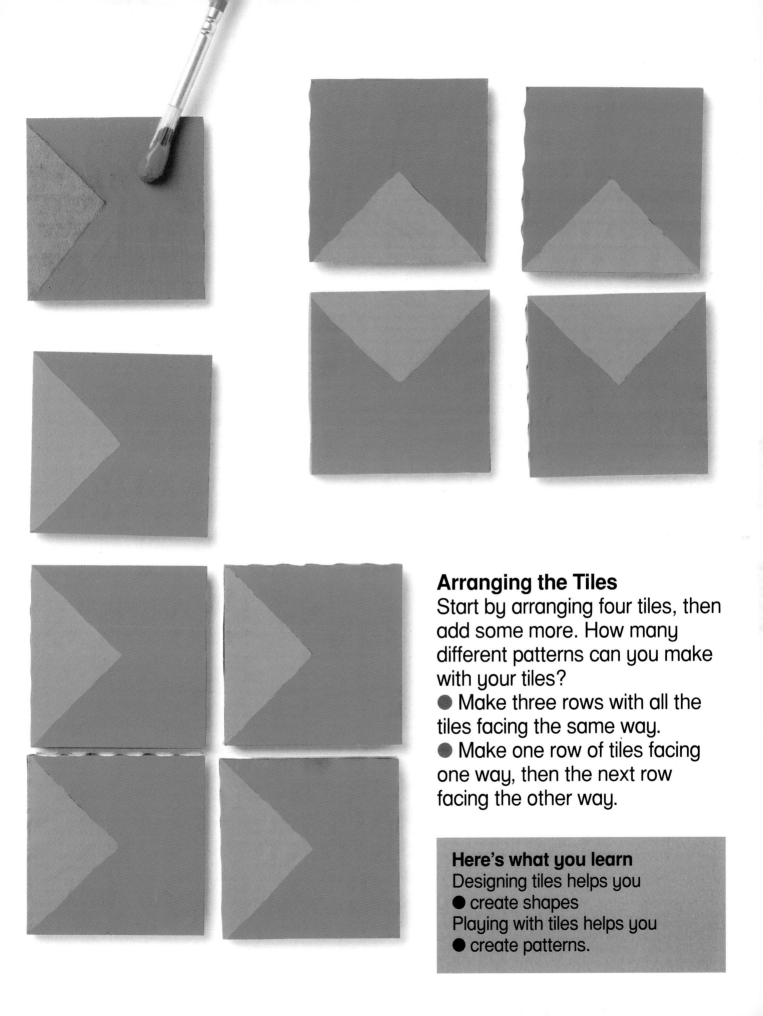

Arranging the Tiles

Start by arranging four tiles, then add some more. How many different patterns can you make with your tiles?

● Make three rows with all the tiles facing the same way.

● Make one row of tiles facing one way, then the next row facing the other way.

Here's what you learn
Designing tiles helps you
● create shapes
Playing with tiles helps you
● create patterns.

These coloured shapes fit together to make patterns.

Making the Shapes

Ask a grown-up to cut some shapes from coloured paper or thin card. They could draw around the shapes shown on this page.

Fitting Together

● Sort the shapes out. Put all the triangles together, all the diamonds, and so on.

● See how the shapes that are the same fit together. Use different colours to make a pattern.

● Now try fitting two different shapes together. Which shapes fit well?

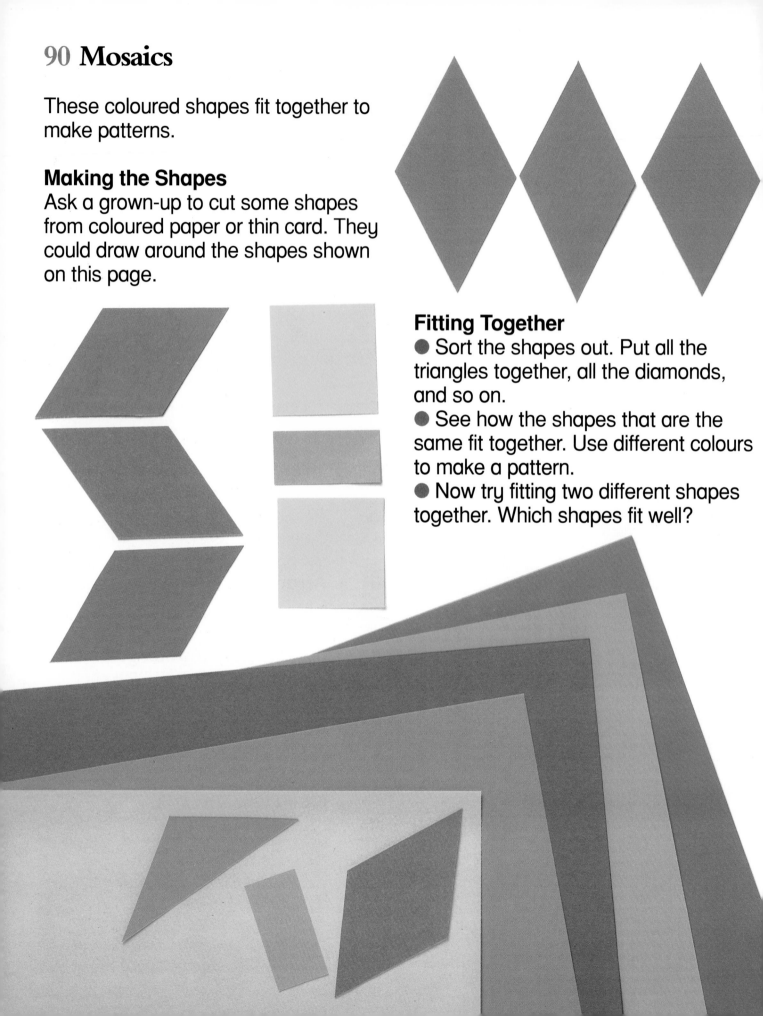

Here's what you learn
Making mosaics helps you
● create patterns
● discover how some shapes fit together, or tessellate.

Make a sheet of wrapping paper by decorating it with a pattern. Pick a shape and repeat it lots of times.

String Blocks
● Glue a long length of string on to a piece of card and let it dry.
● Dip the string into thick paint and press on to a sheet of paper.

Potato Prints
● Think of a simple shape and draw it on a piece of paper. Ask a grown-up to cut your shape from half of a potato so that the shape sticks up.
● Use a paintbrush to cover the shape with thick paint. Press the potato on to a sheet of paper.
● Lift the potato off and put some more paint on. Print the shape lots of times.

Stencils
● Cut a stencil out of strong card.
● Place the stencil on a sheet of paper. Dab paint over the stencil. Remove it carefully and repeat.

Here's what you learn
Making wrapping paper helps you
● create repeating patterns
● create shapes
● invent new designs.

94 Mirror Prints

These amazing prints are reflections.

Fold and Paint
● Fold a piece of paper in half. Open it out and put a blob of paint on it.
● Fold the paper in half again and press down firmly. Then open it out.

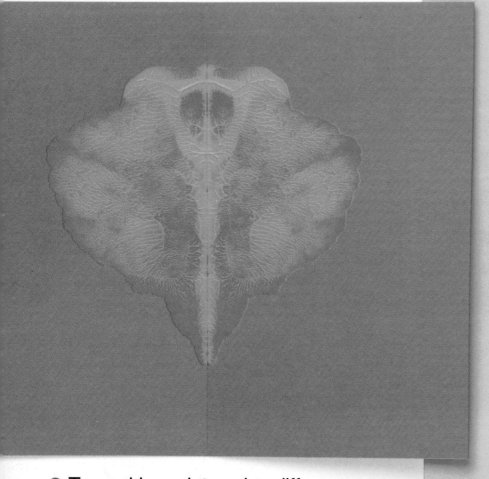

● Try making prints using different colours. Allow one colour to dry before adding the next.

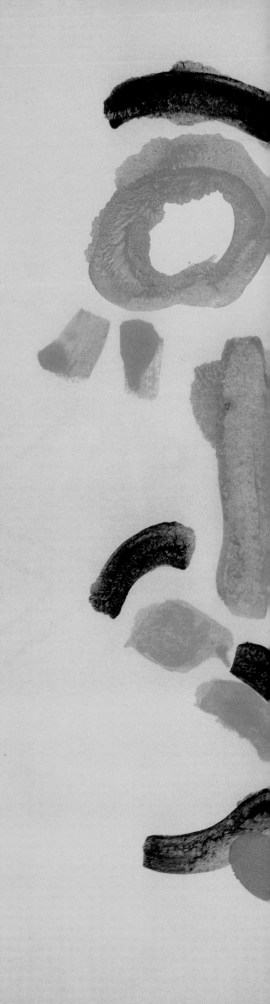

Here's what you learn
Making mirror prints helps you
● discover reflective symmetry
● learn about left and right.

Think up some fabulous patterns to decorate your T-shirts or socks. Use fabric paints, and make sure you read the instructions before you start.

Potato Patterns

● Ask a grown-up to cut a simple shape from half a potato.
● Cover the shape with paint, then press it on to your sock or T-shirt. Repeat to make a pattern.

Here's what you learn
These potato patterns help you
● create repeating patterns
● use familiar shapes
● invent new designs.

Try using different types of patterns to decorate cards, writing paper and envelopes. Use brightly coloured paper and make sure you leave enough room to write on! You could use some of the patterns you have found in this book, or make up some new ones.

● Cut or tear coloured paper shapes. Glue them down in a pattern.
● Use plastic shapes to print.
● Cut out a card stencil. Hold it down firmly and dab on thin paint with a sponge.

Here's what you learn
Decorating stationery helps you
● create patterns
● create shapes
● invent new designs.

Games

Here's a way to make your own pack of playing cards.

Make It – Shape Cards

● Choose four different colours of card. Cut out six rectangles from each.

● Start with one set of six matching cards. Put some paint on a eraser and print once on one card, twice on the next, and so on until you reach six.

● Print one to six on the other sets of cards. When all the cards are printed, you will have a pack.

● Leave your cards to dry before you start playing.

Here's what you learn
Making snap cards helps you
● count to 6.
Playing snap helps you
● recognize number patterns
● match numbers.

Play It – Snap!
● Share the cards out between yourself and one or two friends.
● Take it in turns to lay a card face up on the table.
● When two cards with the same number come together, shout SNAP! You win all the cards on the table.
● If one player runs out of cards, the others keep turning up their cards.
● The game ends when one player wins all the cards.

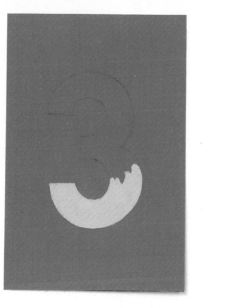

Make It – Number Cards

Make a pack of cards with numbers like these. Choose four colours of card and cut nine rectangles out of each colour. Paint the numbers 1 to 9 on each set of cards.

Simple Rummy

You can play this game with two to four players.

● Deal four cards to each player.

● Put the rest of the pack face down on the table. Turn the top card over and put it next to the pack.

● The aim is to collect a run of three cards. You could pick cards which have numbers next to one another, like 1, 2, 3 or 3, 4, 5. Or you could pick cards which all have the same number.

● The first player picks a card up from the pack or takes the card which is face up.
● The player then throws away one of the cards from their hand by putting it face up on the pile.

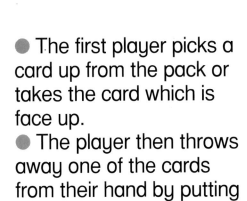

Here's what you learn
Making rummy cards helps you
● write numbers.
Playing rummy helps you
● recognize numbers
● put numbers in order.

It's easy to make this memory game and fun to play it. Any number of players can play together..

Make It

● You will need nine paper cups. Each cup should have a completely different pattern. You could use paint or coloured paper to decorate them.

● When the paint is dry, send everyone out of the room while someone who is not playing prepares the game.

● Place two sweets under two of the cups, three under another two, four under two more and five under two more. You can put any number you like under the last cup.

Play It

- When the game is ready everyone comes back into the room. Take it in turns to lift up two cups.
- If the number of sweets matches, take the sweets and remove the cups from the game. Don't eat the sweets yet!
- If the number of sweets does not match, put the cups back.
- The winner is the player with the most sweets at the end.

Here's what you learn
Playing the memory game helps you
- recognize number patterns
- match numbers.

Up to four people can play this matching numbers game.

Make It – Game Card

● For each player, cut out a rectangle of card like the one below.
● Divide each rectangle into squares.
● Stick coloured paper on to each square.

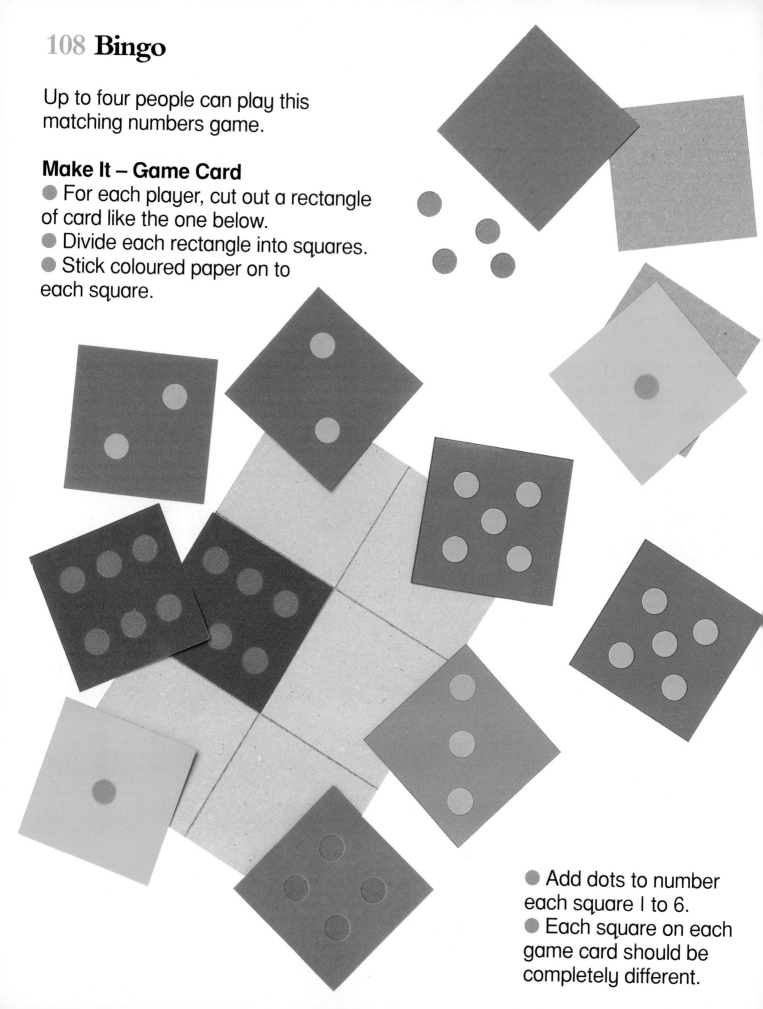

● Add dots to number each square 1 to 6.
● Each square on each game card should be completely different.

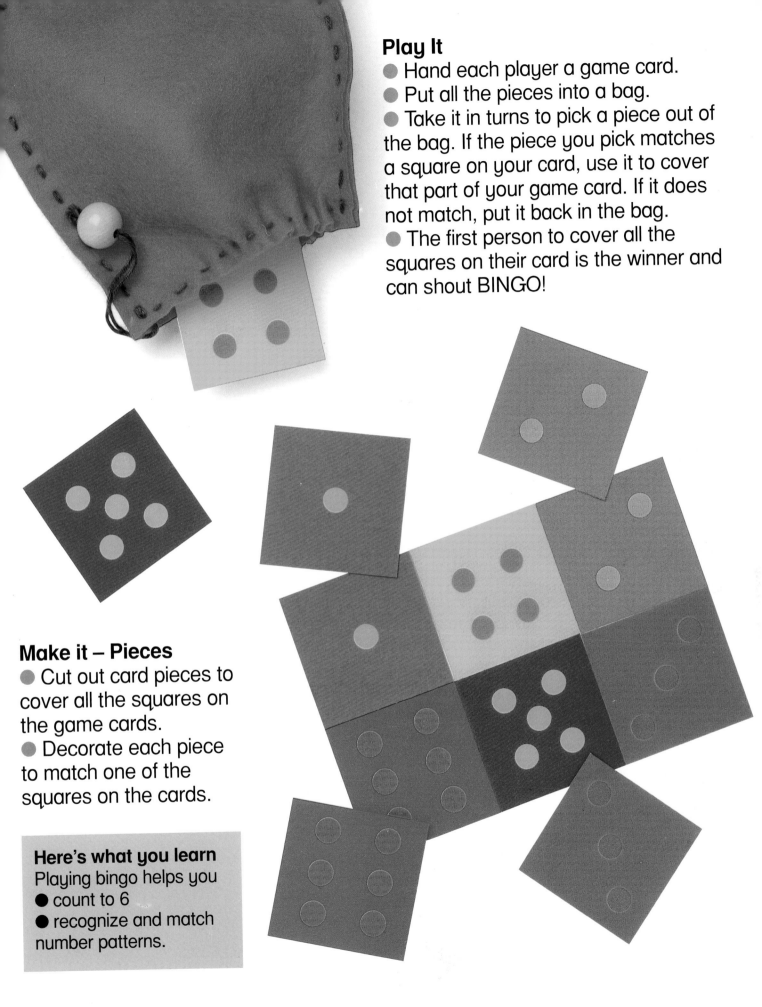

Play It
● Hand each player a game card.
● Put all the pieces into a bag.
● Take it in turns to pick a piece out of the bag. If the piece you pick matches a square on your card, use it to cover that part of your game card. If it does not match, put it back in the bag.
● The first person to cover all the squares on their card is the winner and can shout BINGO!

Make it – Pieces
● Cut out card pieces to cover all the squares on the game cards.
● Decorate each piece to match one of the squares on the cards.

Here's what you learn
Playing bingo helps you
● count to 6
● recognize and match number patterns.

Make It – Pattern Bingo

Make the game cards and pattern pieces in the same way as before. We made our patterns from coloured paper, but you could paint or print them on.

Play It

● Each player chooses a game card.
● Spread the game pieces out face down on the table. Take it in turns to turn over a piece.
● If the piece you pick matches a square on your game card, you can use it to cover that square.

If not, put it back face down, exactly where you found it.
● The winner is the one who covers their card first.

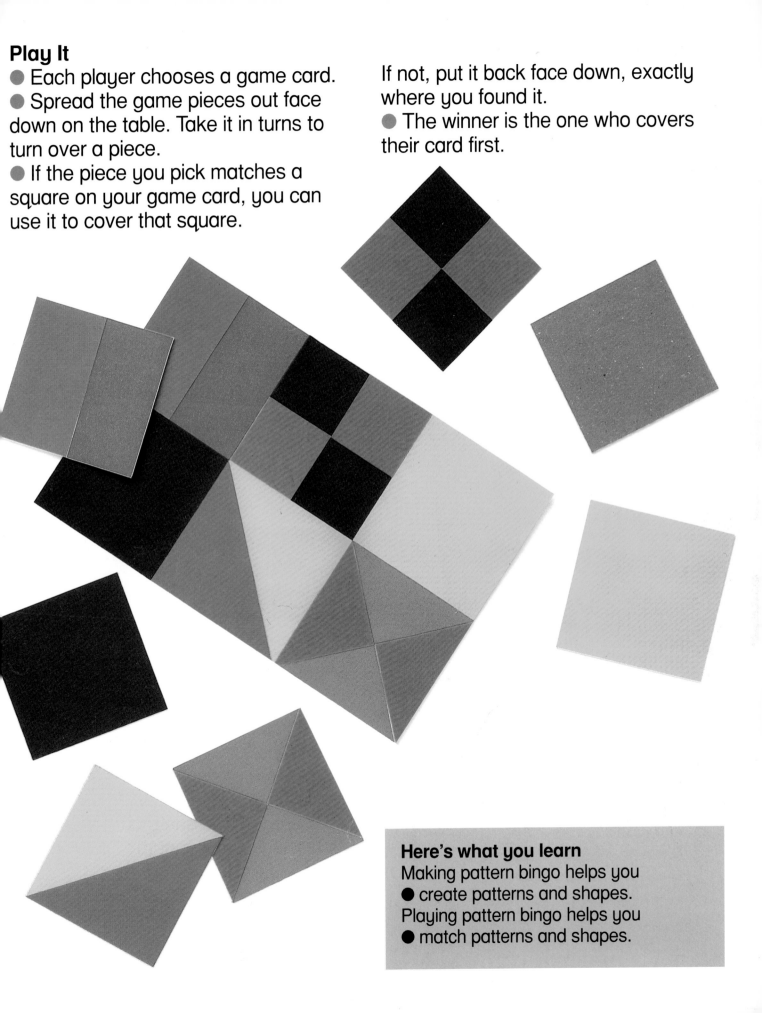

Here's what you learn
Making pattern bingo helps you
● create patterns and shapes.
Playing pattern bingo helps you
● match patterns and shapes.

Try making a set of dominoes. The ones on the opposite page are a complete set.

Make It – Number Dominoes
● Cut out 28 rectangles from a piece of card.
● Stick on circles of paper or paint dots to number your dominoes.
● Make sure you follow the number patterns shown opposite.

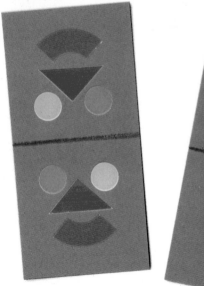

Make It – Funny Faces
You could make a set of dominoes with funny faces instead of numbers.
● One eye on its own = 1
● Two eyes = 2
● Two eyes and one mouth = 3
● Two eyes, one mouth and one nose = 4
● Two eyes, one mouth, one nose and one eyebrow = 5
● The whole face = 6

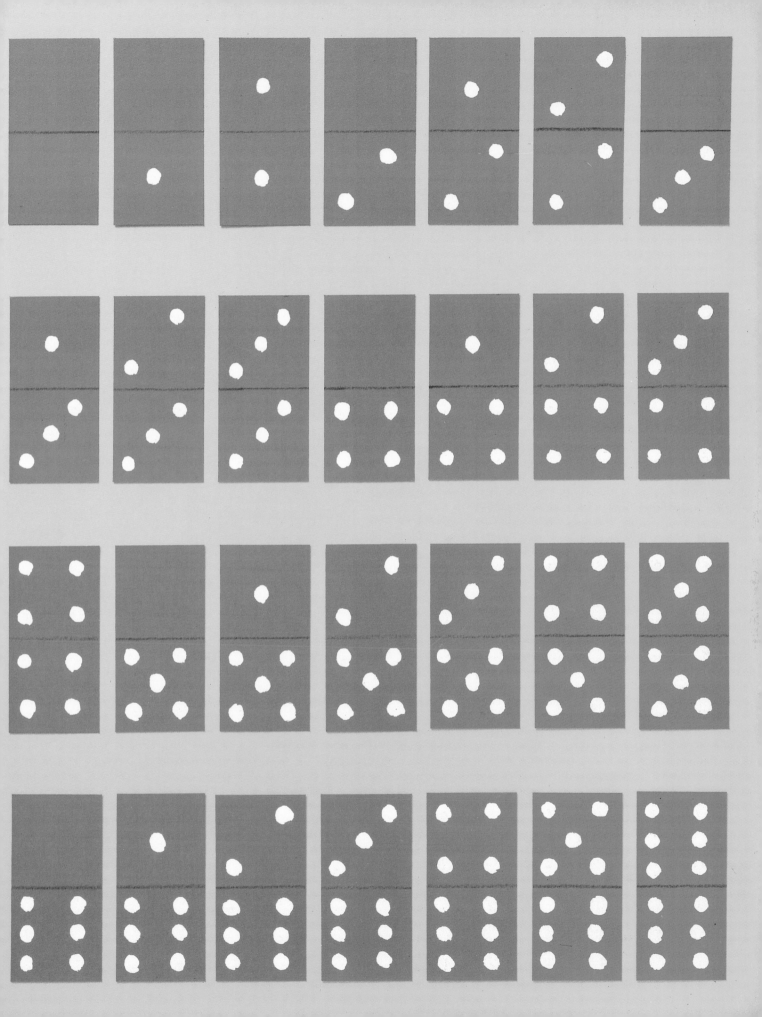

Play It

● Spread out a set of dominoes face down on the table.

● Each player takes an equal number of dominoes, six for two players, five for three players and four for four players. Push the other dominoes to the edge of the table.

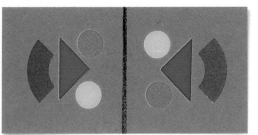

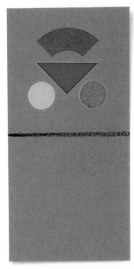

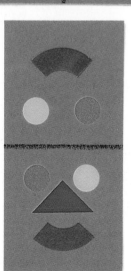

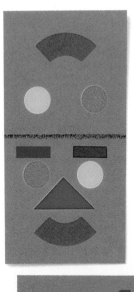

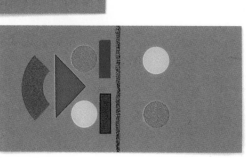

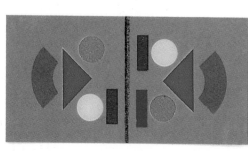

● Take it in turns to start the game.

● The first player places one domino face up on the table. The next player must put a matching domino at one end of it.

- If you do not have a matching domino when it is your turn, you pick one up from the table. If this matches, you can put it down. If not, you keep it and wait for your next turn.
- A domino with two matching numbers can be put sideways. Three dominoes can be joined to it, one in the middle and one at each end.
- The winner is the first player to put down all the dominoes in their hand.

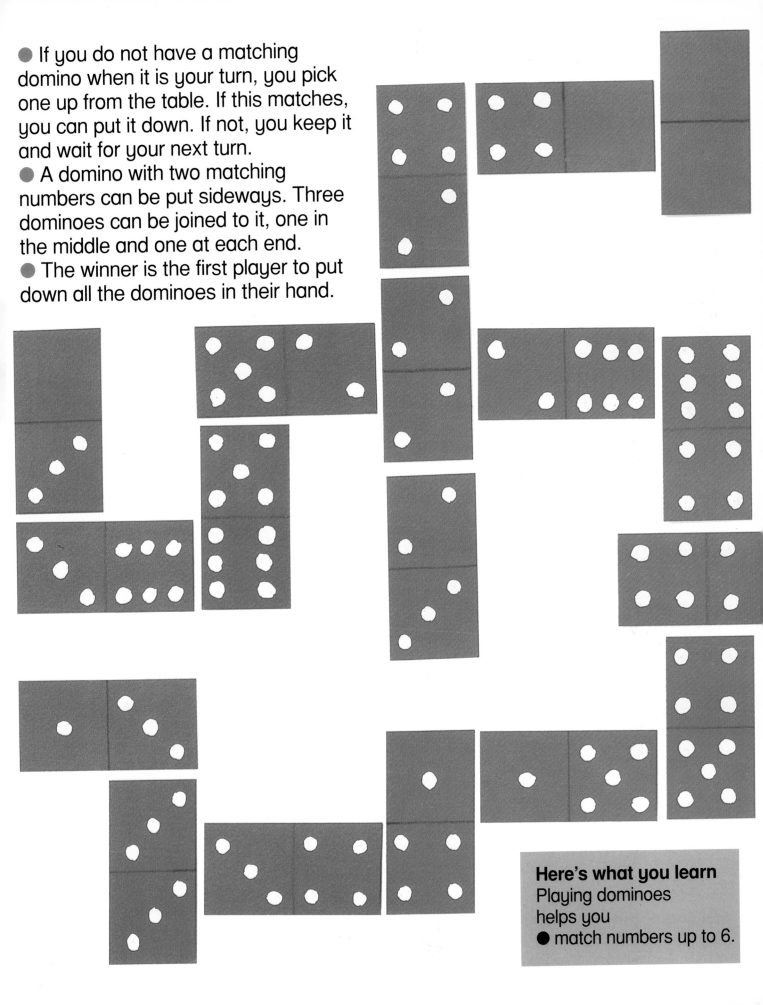

Here's what you learn
Playing dominoes helps you
- match numbers up to 6.

For some games, you need a die or a spinner to help you pick numbers.

Make it – Dice
You can make dice out of lots of different things. When you have made one, number the sides 1 to 6.

● Find a brightly coloured building block. Paint on the dots using a different colour.

● Ask a grown-up to cut two corners off a cardboard box, such as a cereal packet. Slide the pieces together and glue them to make a cube. Paint the cube and stick on paper dots.

● Make a round ball from self-hardening clay. Flatten the sides by pressing a ruler on to the clay. Make tiny balls from different-coloured clay. Press them on to the cube.

Make It – Spinners

Try using a spinner instead of a die. Spin the shape on its stick. Which side does it rest on when it stops? That is your number.

● Trace around the six-sided shape on the right. Use your trace to cut the shape out from card.

● Draw lines with a pencil and ruler to divide the shape into six triangles.

● Cut out triangles of coloured paper and stick them on the spinner.

● Write 1 to 6 on the sections.

● Use a cocktail stick to make a hole through the spinner. Fix the stick under the spinner with modelling clay.

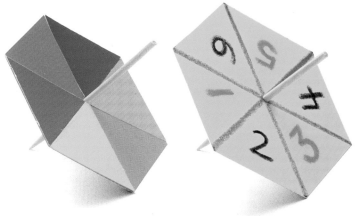

Here's what you learn
Making spinners and dice helps you
● recognize numbers up to 6
● write numbers up to 6.

The object of this game is to be the first player to put together a complete beetle. Each player must have all the parts needed to make up a beetle and you will need one die. The instructions for making the beetle are on the next page.

Legs = 6

Body = 1

Head = 2

Eyes = 3

Antennae = 4

Tail = 5

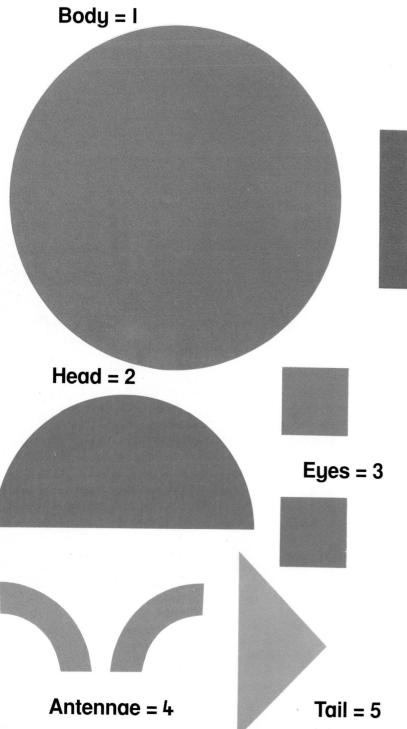

Play It
● Take it in turns to throw the die. To start, you must throw a 1 to get the beetle's body.
● Collect the other parts of the beetle when you throw the right number.
● You may not take the eyes and antennae until you have the head.
● The first player to have a complete beetle wins the game!

Here's what you learn
Playing the beetle game helps you
● recognize numbers up to 6
● learn about chance.

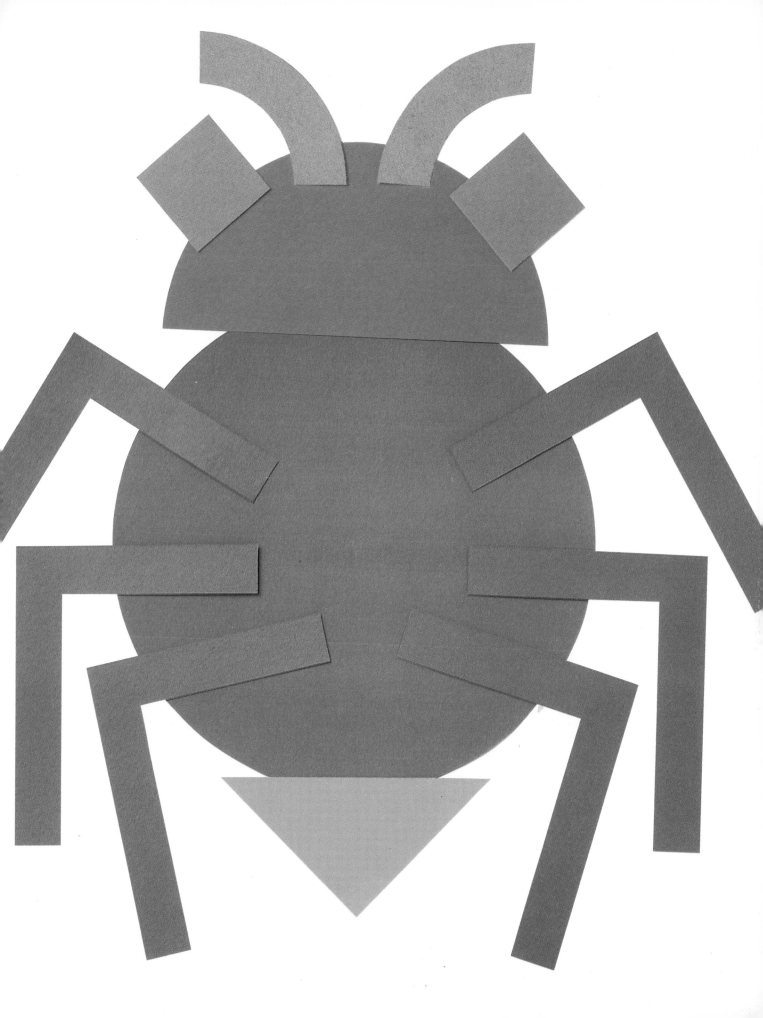

Make It – Beetle

We made our beetle from pieces of coloured card. All the parts can be made from squares and circles.

● You might find it easier to make your beetle by tracing round the shapes on the previous page.

● Each player needs all the parts of the beetle to play the game.

Body

Cut a large circle from coloured card. You could draw around a plate.

Tail

Cut a small square from card. Make a diagonal fold so that you have two triangles. Cut along the fold. You now have two tail pieces.

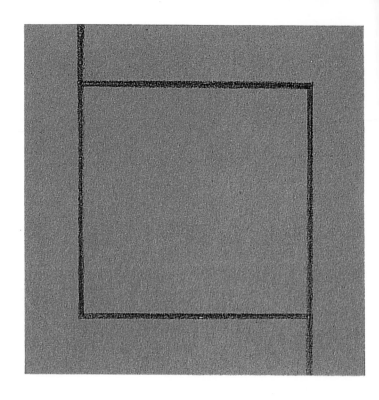

Legs

Cut a square from coloured card. Mark two 'L' shapes inside the square as shown above. Cut out the 'L' shapes to make two legs. Do the same thing with two more squares to make six legs.

Here's what you learn

Making the beetle game helps you
● learn the names of shapes
● draw shapes.

Eyes

Use the left-over squares from the legs to make eyes. Each square will make about four eyes.

Head

Cut a circle smaller than the one used for the body. For example, if you used a dinner plate for the body, you could use a saucer for the head. Fold it in half and cut across the fold to make two semi-circles.

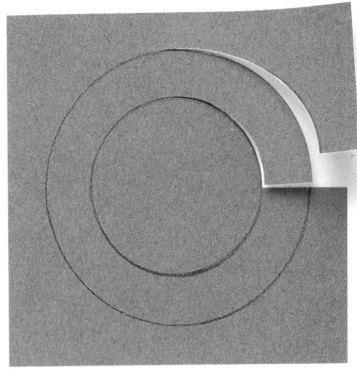

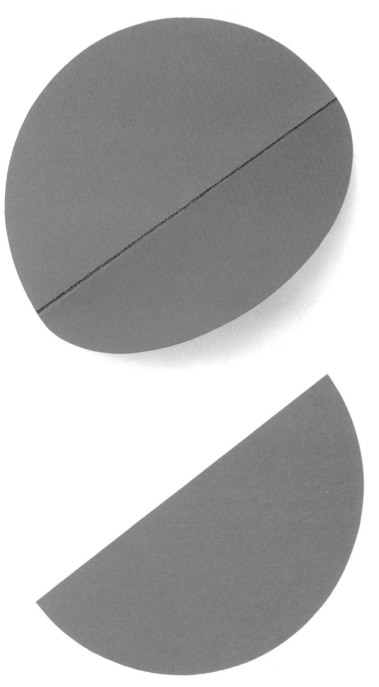

Antennae

Use a small round object, such as a jam jar lid, to draw round. Mark a smaller circle inside with a pencil. Cut through the two circles as shown in the picture. Then cut round the inside and the outside of the circles to make a ring. Fold the ring in half and cut along the fold. Fold each section in half again and cut along the folds.

Once you have made a board, you can play lots of different games.

Make It – Board
● Cut out a piece of cardboard to use as a board.
● Draw lines to divide it up. Stick on coloured paper squares
● Put numbers on the squares.

36 35 34 33 1 32 31 30 29 28 27 26 25 24 23 22 21

Make It – Counters
For some games, each player needs a few matching counters. For others, you need only one counter each. Try using sweets, buttons, corks, or shells.

Here's what you learn
Making a game board helps you
● recognize numbers up to 36.

Make It – Slit and Slot Counters
Instead of finding counters, you could make your own.
● Cut out two matching shapes from stiff paper.
● Cut a slit from the bottom of one shape to the middle.
● Cut a slit in the other shape from the top to the middle.
● Slot the two shapes together to make a counter that stands up!

Play It – Forward and Back

For this game you will need to make a spinner like the one shown on the board below. Mark the blue sections 4, 5 and 6, and the green sections 1, 2 and 3. You will also need a board and one counter for each player.

● Spin the spinner to see who starts.

● Blue numbers make you go forwards and green make you go backwards.

● If you move backwards off the board you have to get a blue number before you can get on again.

● The winner is the first to reach the end of the board.

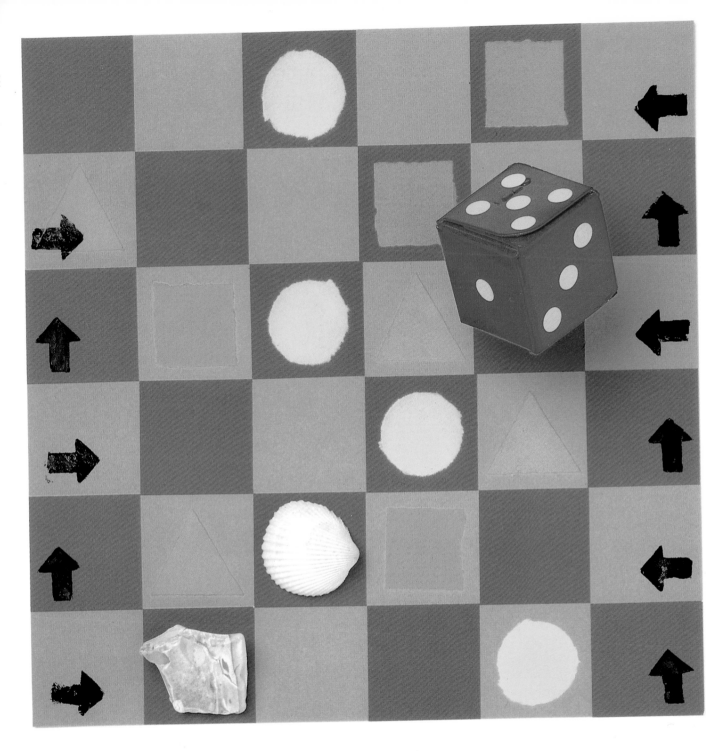

Hazards

Work your way around this board
following the arrows.

● If you land on a pink square, go
forward four spaces.

● If you land on a yellow circle, miss
a turn.

● If you land on an orange triangle,
go forward three spaces.

126 Snakes and Ladders

You need a board with coloured squares to play snakes and ladders.

Make It – Snakes

● Mix two colours of modelling clay into a ball. Roll the ball into a sausage. Flatten the head slightly and add two eyes. Curve your snake into a wiggly shape.

Make It – Ladders

● Cut a long strip of coloured paper. Make folds along the length of the paper. Make some short and some long ladders.

Play It

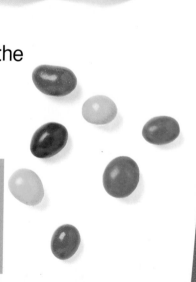

● Throw a die to move. If you land at the bottom of a ladder climb up it. If it is a snake's head, slide down it.
● The first player to the end wins.

Here's what you learn
Playing this game helps you
● recognize numbers up to 6
● learn about chance.

Index & Notes

Action Maths and the National Curriculum

Creating the shapes and patterns, using the units of measurement, and making and playing the games shown in this book will be directly helpful to National Curriculum mathematics. Doing these activities involves interpreting and carrying out instructions, appraising work, and developing confidence in craft skills. Thus, children's involvement in other National Curriculum subjects, such as science, technology and art can be supported by having fun with this book.

Contents

Consultants

Wendy and David Clemson are experienced teachers and researchers. They have written many successful books on mathematics and are regular contributors to 'eG', the educational supplement of *The Guardian* newspaper. Wendy is currently pursuing her interests in the primary curriculum and is working on a variety of writing projects for children, parents and teachers, with a particular emphasis on the early years. David is Reader in Primary Education at Liverpool John Moores University.